G000118302

THE CROSSING
OF THE CONWY

The Crossing of the Conwy

and its role in the story of northern Wales

Michael Senior

with a Foreword by Sir Wyn Roberts

© Text: Michael Senior

Copyright © by Llygad Gwalch 2008
All rights reserved. No part of this publication may be reproduced,
stored in a retrieval system, or transmitted in any form or by
any means, electronic, electrostatic, magnetic tape, mechanical,
photocopying, recording, or otherwise, without prior
permission of the authors of the works herein.

ISBN: 978-1-84524-066-0

Cover design: Sian Parri

First published in 1996 by
Gwasg Carreg Gwalch, 12 Iard yr Orsaf, Llanrwst,
Wales LL26 0EH.
☎ 01492 642031   ▤ 01492 641502
🖰 llyfrau@carreg-gwalch.com Website: www.carreg-gwalch.com

New edition: 2009
Llygad Gwalch, Ysgubor Plas, Llwyndyrys,
Pwllheli, Gwynedd LL53 6NG
☎ 01758 750432   ▤ 01758 750438
🖰 llyfrau@carreg-gwalch.com Website: www.carreg-gwalch.com

Contents

Preface to the revised edition

Of all my books *The Crossing of the Conwy* had the most promising birth. It was launched on the day the tunnel was opened and the signing event was part of Project Conwy's programme for the day. Normally nobody, except family and friends, and with luck the Press photographer, turns up to a book singing. This time, when I got to the Project Conwy office in Castle Street there was a queue, stretching across their admittedly rather small room and into the street. I was late arriving, but I had a good excuse. I had been having lunch with the Queen.

I and some two hundred others. Tucked away in a corner of the marquee set up in the Vicarage car park, we could just about see Her Majesty, who seemed to be enjoying herself, and was clearly in no hurry to go.

It is the fact that the Queen was there that day that is of significance. It was a recognition of the importance of the Conwy crossing. Her Majesty's presence symbolised the historic nature of what had taken place: the construction of Britain's first immersed tube tunnel.

When I wrote *The Crossing of the Conwy* the tunnel had just been completed, making the A55 into a true through route of motorway scale. As it happens I had played several roles in the lead-up to this, specifically at the long-drawn-out Public Inquiry. In one of these roles I had opposed the whole thing, on the grounds that something of this scale was not required and would have detrimental effects not just on the environment but on the social character of the area. I lost that one, and now, twenty-five years later, we may consider the results. Luckily in another role, representing Conwy Civic Society, I helped to win a more local battle, to get the crossing of the river out of sight under the riverbed.

We can see now that this vast civil engineering project, of which the Conwy river crossing was only one significant phase, has had radical effects, some of which (such as increased prosperity for the area) must be viewed as beneficial. It has opened up a corridor of development along the north Welsh coast. It has undoubtedly made the area easier to get to, though the corollary of that is that it is easier to pass through as well, and there is no doubt that the greatest benefit falls outside north Wales, on those who wish to pass from England to Ireland without being delayed. An increase in the demand for country property, and hence in the value of it, would perhaps have taken place anyway, since this has always been an area which attracted an imported and retirement population. This natural trend has no doubt been accelerated, and influence, financial and cultural, from across the border has no doubt been enabled by the road to extend further into rural Wales.

The loss of the indigenous cultural identity, to which we pointed as a danger in the 1970s, may perhaps (thankfully) have been averted by its own reaction to the threat, since it is in many ways rediscovering and re-establishing itself. It is common now to hear Welsh spoken in the coastal towns, once a matter of some surprise.

The matter of the crossing of the Conwy has always been related to the distinction between the more

Anglicised lands in the direction of Chester and the mountainous Welsh heartland. The geological fault which the river represents acts as a line drawn between two worlds. The physical linking of the two, first by Telford and now by tunnel, might appear to blur that boundary, but I think this is partly an illusion. The river remains the symbol of a psychological divide, a passage which has always, in the past, been hard to cross.

As I remark somewhere in this book: few rivers of its size can have had so much impact on their area's history.

Michael Senior
Glan Conwy
December 2006

Foreword

The river Conwy is not primarily one of those rivers that are 'roads which move' and carry us up and down, like the Rhine or the Mississippi. Historically, the Conwy has always been a barrier and a challenge to those who wished to cross it, especially from the east – the Romans, the mediaeval English and Norman kings and later, travellers to north-western Wales and Ireland. How they tackled the crossing, fared in the course of it and how the crossing affected local people and the environment is a continuing story and the opening of the tunnel crossing in 1991 is only the latest episode in the fascinating saga narrated by Michael Senior in this book.

Having been the Member of Parliament for Conwy for twenty-one years and the Welsh Office Minister responsible for roads since 1985, I have taken a very close interest in the decision-making process that finally led to the choice of the tunnel option as opposed to a bridge crossing which would have dwarfed the castle had a bridge been built alongside the existing bridges, or dominated the much loved and cherished seaward view had a bridge been built from Deganwy over the narrows.

The tunnel represents a triumph for sensitivity and awareness of the unique character of the built heritage of the castle and its natural setting on the west bank of the Conwy estuary; it also represents a superb reconciliation between the need to conserve this beautiful and irreplaceable environment with the imperatives of a safe and speedy modern transportation system.

The walled town of Conwy, Deganwy where there

was one another castle, Llandudno Junction where the branch lines diverge to Llandudno and up the Conwy Valley, and Glan Conwy, once the main river port; all these places and their people face a future as diverse and varied in possibilities and opportunities as their past has been, because there is a new way of crossing the Conwy and that will affect us all – one way or another.

Sir Wyn Roberts
(Subsequently Lord Roberts of Conwy)

Introduction

For quite some time a combination of political and commercial factors had led to the piecemeal upgrading of the Holyhead road. Only the northern Wales sections remained below standard, and plans and works were put in hand to improve even these. There remained the problem of the crossing of the Conwy. Under the pressure of increasing urgency various imaginative and costly engineering schemes were considered and debated, at some length and in conditions of increasing controversy. At last a bold solution was agreed on, unique in Britain for its innovatory technique, massive in its scale, and unique in its imaginative response to the sensitive demands of its location.

That was in 1811. Not much, one might think, has changed. Telford's bridge and causeway became at once one of the wonders of the engineering world. The problems giving rise to this solution also, in their turn, have a familiar look about them. A new European political background, namely the Act of Union of Britain and Ireland of 1800, had given rise to new demands for travel, a new significance to the link between London and Dublin. This combined with greatly increased commercial traffic arising from the expansion of trade caused by the Industrial Revolution. There was a general demand at the time for greater speed of movement.

Unfortunately much of the work then undertaken, and the main role of the bridge itself, went out of date at once, overtaken by the speed of change of which they were, ironically, a part. For reasons we shall see, traffic switched to other routes. In the course of this review of the history of travel on the northern Wales coast and the problem of the crossing of the Conwy we shall see ample proof of the truism that history repeats itself. What is most reliably repeated, it seems, is unexpected change. Telford, after all, could never have foreseen the replacement of the horse by automobility.

Now as we contemplate the start of a new phase of this story, we may well wonder what unpredicted events are about to overtake us.

The latest episode in the history of the crossing of the Conwy river was completed. The first immersed-tube tunnel in Britain forms the last link of Euroroute 22, and, after the Channel tunnel, represented the biggest engineering project in Europe at the time. Though very much a part of the modern age it had in common with previous episodes in the history of the river crossing one persistent characteristic: it was both the result of changes in the pattern of Welsh communications and settlement patterns as a whole and destined to be the cause of greater ones.

Historic events have a historical context. If we view this latest engineering feat in the light of the long past of the history of the crossing we will see much of Wales' history unfolding from this point of interaction of the road and the river.

1. *The Lie of the Land*

The river Conwy, from its source in a mountain lake to its discharge into Conwy Bay at Deganwy, is a little over twenty-seven miles long. It drains a large upland area, originally a slope of the vast dome culminating in the heights of Snowdon, which includes the Carneddau range and the moorland above Penmachno and Ysbyty Ifan. Its route follows a geological fault and is pre-glacial, the glaciers which subsequently flowed down its valley smoothing it somewhat but surprisingly little straightening its course.

It has long been thought that the river did not always flow to the sea the way it does now, but ran rather down the Mochdre valley to emerge at Penrhyn Bay. This supposition, originally perhaps based on the observable likelihood of the Mochdre valley's being a river valley, predates the evidence from geology which is now available. It was said to have been based on the behaviour of the salmon, which sometimes apparently try to get into the Conwy at Penrhyn Bay. This supposes improbably that salmon somehow have a race memory capable of surviving tens of thousands of years, and, if it occurs, is more easily explained by the fact that salmon frequently make mistakes and enter the 'wrong' river, leaving again to try to find their home waters. Alternatively if they locate their own river by something equal to the smell of its water, some Conwy water may well emerge at Penrhyn Bay through its connecting stream the Afon Ganol and thus mislead them.

This old legend is however now supported by

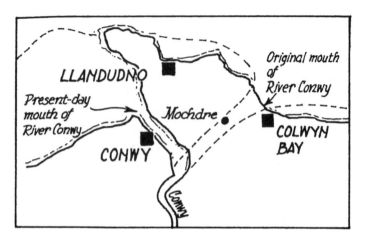

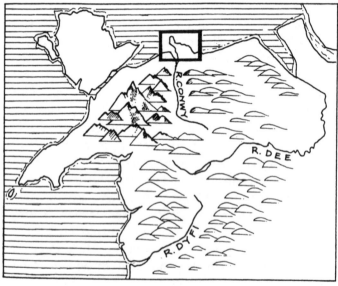

geological evidence, as well as by visible probability.

Until conduited to clear a route for the new road, the river in the Mochdre valley, the Afon Ganol, could be seen to run both ways, disgorging at both Penrhyn Bay and into the Conwy, presumably according to the state of the tide at both its ends. For hundreds of years during the historical period the whole of the area between Penrhyn Bay and Glan Conwy Corner was marsh – hence the name of the district, 'Rhos', meaning a moor or plain. It remained treacherous and probably impassable until a causeway was built across it by monks, presumably to link the Abbey of Aberconwy to the monastic settlement at Rhos Fynach, and therefore before the Abbey moved in 1283.

At the time of the glacial period and before it is thought that a rock ridge joined the Vardre, above Deganwy, to Conwy Mountain, blocking off that possible exit to the sea. At the end of the ice ages, as the glaciers began to melt for the last time, great blocks of ice drifted southwards from the Scottish coast and grounded on the northern coast of Wales. We know this because of the deposits which they left, including boulders dropped on our northern hillsides, 'glacial erratics', which do not originate in Wales.

This ice-flow, known as 'Irish Sea ice', would very probably have blocked off the Conwy's original discharge at Penrhyn Bay. If so, a vast lake would then be formed, between the coastal ice and the melting mountain glacier. That the Conwy valley was submerged under such a lake for a long period is indicated by the thickness of apparent lake deposits which form part of the valley floor today.

The Conwy now flows into Conwy Bay
through a narrow gap at Deganwy

At some point during the melting process the ridge across the present mouth seems to have been eroded (by the land glacier or Irish Sea ice, or both) and finally broken through, and what remained of the inland glacier then flowed out that way, leaving moraine and boulder clay beyond Deganwy. The Conwy river followed it, and

It is thought that the original Conwy estuary
flowed eastwards through the Mochdre valley

the Mochdre valley silted up, to become the diminishing
stream of the Afon Ganol running through its marsh.

An alternative scenario, in the light of our current
knowledge (or ignorance), is that it was the glacier itself
which blocked the Deganwy exit, by depositing there its
burden of moraine and boulder clay, forcing an outflow

through the Mochdre valley. That could then have remained the course of the river perhaps until post-geological times, or until whenever it was that the barrier at Deganwy was worn away by tides and floods. In either chronology we have to think of the river Conwy as having had alternative outlets to the sea.

This much we can speculate from the geology. When we approach history, a different puzzle confronts us. The ambiguity as to the Conwy's route is matched by an ambiguity about its name.

The earliest direct evidence which we have for the name is clearly inscribed on the Roman milestone found near Llanfairfechan in 1883, now in the British Museum. There we read, in the cryptic abbreviations used by the Romans:

IMP. CAES. TRAI
ANVS. HADRIANVS
AVG. P.M. TR. P.V
, P.P. COS. III
A. KANOVIO
. M.P. VIII

This gives us the date as being the third consulship (Cos. III) of Hadrian ('the Emperor Caesar Trajan Hadrian Augustus'), mentioning also several other titles, which would locate the erection of the stone at AD 121-2, the year of the Emperor Hadrian's visit to Britain. At the bottom the stone bears the statement A. KANOVIO M.P. VIII, that is, eight 'mille passuum', 'thousand paces', or miles, to Kanovium.

We shall find this form 'kan', or 'can', occurring again, in early names at the river's mouth, such as Gannow and Cannok, which seem to be related to the present name Deganwy. It has also been speculated that the name Deganwy comes from that of the British tribe which occupied this area, sometimes given as Decanti. They are referred to by Tacitus as Decangi, and their own name for themselves seems (from inscribed pieces of lead found in their territory) to have been 'Deceangli'. It is impossible to say which way the causal chain might have gone, connecting the names of the river, the tribe, and the town at the river's mouth. All we can do is note the double incidence (in Tacitus and on the milestone) as early as the Roman period of the syllable 'can'.

However from comparatively early times the form 'con' also occurs; in the Antonine Itinerary, a Roman road book originally drawn up in the second century but (in the form in which we have it) amended later, the distance from Segontium (Caernarfon) to 'Conovio' is given as twenty-three miles.

The next source is a work known as the Ravenna Cosmography, a sort of gazeteer written in the seventh century. Here our Roman fort is known as Canubio, though the 'b' has crept in because the compiler, a monk of Ravenna, was copying from a Greek source, in which the sound of 'v' would be conveyed by 'b'. The 'u' is also thought to be a transcriber's misreading. We are in fact back to Canovio.

The matter is further confused by the use by Camden, in the 16th century, of the spelling 'Cynwy', which seems to have no authentic root in antiquity. This spelling was adopted as the original by Canon Williams in his *History of Aberconwy*. Williams has caused much confusion by presenting his own fanciful conjectures as if they were established fact, and among these is the decision that the form 'Cynwy' was the original one. Having picked up what appears to be an error by Camden, Williams then finds conveniently that it can be translated as 'chief water', from 'cyn', chief, and 'wy', water. As so often this baseless speculation has proved much more popular than the facts, which are admittedly rather scant.

What needs to be explained is how there came to be two forms for the name of the Roman fort and so presumably for the name of the river after which (in the normal Roman habit) the fort would almost certainly have been named. The most authoritative explanation so far produced by scholars is that the form 'can' belongs to the original Celtic language from which Welsh developed, since it can be shown that in other cases 'can' in Celtic becomes 'con' in Welsh. 'Canovio' in the old Celtic language would therefore become 'Conwy' in Welsh. The only thing that is odd, if this theory is accepted, is that the two forms persisted side by side for so long.

What, then, does it probably mean?

There is a Celtic root 'can' meaning fame or glory, which would give the original meaning as 'the renowned river'. It has also been suggested that the 'can' might come from 'cawn', meaning 'reed': the river with reeds. On the whole this view has less support, and is more open to doubt that the 'glory' from 'can' hypothesis. The dominant fact is that the origins of the name of the river remain in doubt. It is most likely a pre-Welsh, Brythonic Celtic name.

The river Conwy lies at a crucial point, from the point of view of land use, settlement and military strategy, between the moderately level country bordering England and the mountainous heartland of Snowdonia, dividing northern Wales vertically into two approximately equal sections. It is no accident, of course, that the country either side of it is so different. It lies where it does because of a sharp change in the geology. The difference between its two banks, however, has had a chain reaction on the area's history.

The land between the Conwy and the Dee is more fertile, richer, and consequently more desirable. It is also easier to overrun. The inner sanctuary of Gwynedd is a hard country to live in, but easy to defend. The Conwy lies between them, underlining this paradox, a small yet daunting barrier. Crossing it, historically, had psychological as well as geographical connotations.

The process of mutual interaction between the crossing of the river and the history of northern Wales is one which increases under its own momentum. As the river affects the wider issues, so the need increases to deal with the problem of the crossing. The whole social and political history of northern Wales has been affected by the fact that the Conwy river is where it is. Few rivers of its size can have had so much impact on their area's history.

2. A Choice of Routes

The natural crossing place of a river is its lowest fording point. Indeed this seems to have been the place where the Conwy was crossed from the very earliest days, since the road across the hills between Ro-wen and Aber was the route said to have been taken by giants, and Geoffrey of Monmouth (one of our earliest historians) tells us that giants became extinct in Britain before the Roman invasion – though whether one should always believe what historians say is another matter.

The story of the giants in fact arises in explanation of some prehistoric stones, which themselves perhaps indicate an ancient trackway. A giant and a giantess, the story goes, were crossing the pass through the hills carrying building stones with which they intended to make a house; he had two large pillars for the doorway, she an apronful of round stones for the walls. Halfway across the pass they met a shoe-mender coming the other way, and asked him how far it was to Anglesey. He had round his neck the string of shoes he was taking home to mend, and, fearful perhaps of the start of a trend of immigration, told them that it was so far that he had worn out all those shoes on the way.

The giantess let loose her apron-load, the giant threw down his two uprights, with expletives which we can imagine, and Anglesey was saved for later invasions. The pile of stones is still there (in fact a Bronze Age burial cairn) and the standing pillars give the pass its name, Bwlch-y-ddeufaen, the pass of the two stones.

Whether or not their purpose is to mark the way, or

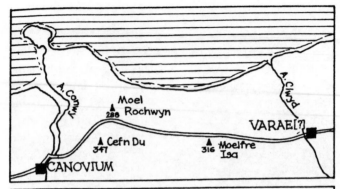

ROMAN ROADS AND FORTS

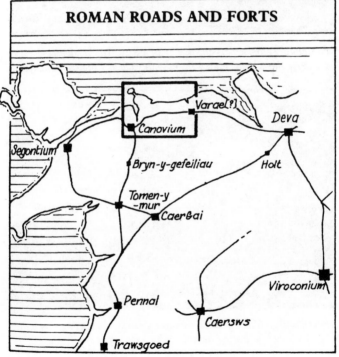

23

Two standing stones mark the line of an ancient trackway crossing the hills above the Conwy, giving the pass the name of Bwlch-y-ddeufaen.

The neolithical Maen-y-bardd chamber stands immediately above the Roman road indicating the use of this route in prehistoric times.

The hill-fort of Pen-y-gaer overlooks the inland crossing of the river used in prehistoric times and by the Romans.

something more obscure, they certainly indicate the use of this route as a crossing of the hills in very early times. Further along the valley slope, above Ro-wen, stands another remarkable testimony, Maen-y-bardd, a neolithic burial chamber. Thus when the Romans in due course crossed the river at Caerhun, in AD 61, they were following a route which had apparently already been in use for some two or three thousand years.

Caer Lleon, on Conwy Mountain, controlled the river's mouth.

We still call it the Roman Road. It passes through open upland now, uninhabited except by sheep. It runs much of the way in the form of a ditch through hill-grass and heather. Yet the same valley contains the signs of numerous hut circles and compounds which indicate that at that time it must have been quite well populated.

Even clearer is the evidence of the Iron Age forts, which were in use before the Romans arrived and in some cases survived into the period of occupation. One of the best stands above the valley, looking down with a startling bird's-eye view onto both the crossing place and the line of the rising road. Pen-y-gaer, with its double walls of stone and earth, controls the valley and the river-crossing just as Caer Lleon, on the top of Conwy Mountain controls the river's mouth.

Indeed this seems to be how these Iron Age hillforts worked, set as they are within sight and easy reach of each other to give maximum protection to the land in between, themselves no doubt places of refuge, probably lightly garrisoned to enable watch to be kept and signals lit. Their existence would have enabled a reasonably secure farming life to emerge in their catchment areas. In our case the neighbours Pen-y-gaer and Caer Lleon set the alternatives for future settlement patterns and for the line of the road: across the valley, or along the coast.

If later decisions had been influenced by the Roman one (as itself it was influenced by the existence of the ancient trackway), rather than by outside factors which we shall be investigating, the consequences would have been considerable. If Edward I had built his castle at Tal-y-cafn, Telford would have crossed there, and there would have been no coastal road or causeway, but rather a major valley town and an empty wooded headland where Conwy now is. The railway would not have attempted to negotiate Bwlch-y-ddeufaen, but would have run instead through mid-Wales to a port for Ireland on the Llŷn peninsula, and instead of the resorts of Colwyn Bay and Llandudno we should have major towns further south and a wild coast here.

It was, as we shall see, a close-run thing. The reasons why the Romans favoured Bwlch-y-ddeufaen kept it in favour for many centuries. It has the benefits of directness in its linking of coast to coast, from a natural crossing-place through a natural pass.

The Romans came to the Conwy valley from their fort at Chester, which became the legionary headquarters of the north-west. At the time of their first venture into northern Wales, in AD 61, the network of forts was not yet established, Chester was only a new staging post for the northern expeditions, and nothing more than a field fort would have been built at the crossing of the Conwy. Nevertheless any major Roman campaign – such as this one – required a road. The line of the route from Chester to the Conwy river, and that across the hills from there to the other coast, was set, and with it the relationship of northern Wales to the area which would in due course become its English neighbour.

To understand why the Romans went to such trouble to press went into Wales, and how they thus found themselves on the Conwy, we have to consider the situation which Ostorius Scapula encountered when he first arrived, in about AD 47, to become the governor and military commander of Britain.

The situation was, Tacitus says plainly, chaotic. All the British tribes were staging guerrilla-style revolts. The part of the province under Roman control was under threat of invasion from the 'unpacified' parts. Ostorius decided on the drastic task of disarming the rebels, itself an unpopular move which led to further unrest. The war went on for nine years, until the great British leader Caractacus was taken prisoner on the northern Wales border near the Severn valley.

Ostorius died, worn out, and the two governors who in turn succeeded him presided over an unstable, and often deteriorating, situation. Suetonius Paulinus then took over in about the year 59. He was an expert in mountain warfare and a remarkably determined man. Two years of success in pushing the frontiers of the pacified area outwards, establishing forts to keep them there, and of course building those great roads between those forts, led him to undertake the ultimate ambitious thrust. The island of Anglesey, Tacitus tells us, 'was feeding the native resistance'. He probably meant that in two senses: as *Môn, Mam Cymru*, 'Mother of Wales', it provided the surrounding hills with grain; and as the centre of the old religion it fed the morale and the self-identity of the Britons.

That first venture across the Conwy was, however, not a great success. With the general and the army so far away the Iceni, in the south-east, rose against the Romans, under their fearsome queen Boudicca, or Boadicea. Suetonius and the army made a forced march southwards, and Anglesey, though its grain and sacred groves were largely destroyed, remained unoccupied.

It seems likely, however, that a small force was left at the fort, Canovium, on the river Conwy. If so, both it and the road would have been ready for use by the next campaign, sparked off by the next major event. It is this more determined and permanent Roman invasion which set the basic pattern for northern Wales' history.

In the late summer of the year 77, the Romans suffered a blow which threatened to flatten their already flagging morale. The tribe known to the Romans as the Ordovices, who occupied the northern part of mid-Wales, succeeded in ambushing and massacring an outpost of Roman cavalry. Evidently they then fled into the hills of northern

Wales, knowing that the Roman troops moved with more difficulty there, and, with autumn and winter approaching, that they had the climate as well as the terrain on their side.

It happened that the timing of these events involved the effect of personality, since the newly-arrived governor of Britain was Agricola, and he was a person capable of courageous decision. He gathered the scattered legions, and marched into the hills.

Chester was then a newly-built fort, the home of the Second Auxiliary Legion, and it was almost certainly from that base that Agricola campaigned. Having chased the Ordovices to their hillforts, and wiped out a large part of their fighting force, he decided to establish Roman order in these far west parts, to reduce the risk of such things happening again. Once again the Romans invaded Anglesey, and although they did not at that time settle on the island they were, as a governing presence, in northern Wales to stay. Far west at the mouth of the Seiont they built the fort of Segontium, today Caernarfon; and here on the Conwy the crucial crossing was defended by a fortress on the further, western bank, Canovium.

The crossing itself may actually have been a little downstream of the fort, at Tal-y-cafn, since there are signs that the line of the road dropped to the valley there and ran northwards along the western bank; but this is not the certain route, since for much of its length the road from the river eastwards has simply disappeared. Excavations have however found enough parts of it to give us some confidence of its general line and a fairly detailed knowledge of its form of construction. In the presumably

The Romans built a fort to defend their river crossing – Canovium, now Caerhun.

much-used stretches near Chester it was laid on a bed of sandstone slabs, but further west it consisted of round pebbles hammered into clay and bounded by kerb stones. It appears to have been paved, at least in some stretches, with small flat stones – although some of the paving, which may still be seen in parts of the untouched uplands lengths, may well be of later date. We have to remember that this road was still in use until the early 19th century.

From a map one can see at a glance the Roman strategy of bracketing the heartland of northern Wales with a ring of forts about a day's journey apart, linked by a network of roads. At the key centres, Canovium and Segontium, these forts could be supplied by sea from Chester, a feature which further strengthened their ability to support each other. Interestingly all these features were to be repeated with modifications a thousand years later, but the later master strategist, Edward I.

If the establishment of a crossing point of the Conwy river dates from the winter of 77 to 78 AD, there is not much to see of that first crossing now. Agricola's fort would have been made of wood, and the remains which have been identified at Caerhun, the site of Canovium, date from the early second century when it was expanded in stone. Garrisoned by the tenth legion, the outpost remained an important settlement until the start of the 120s, when pressure on the north involved the movement of manpower to construct Hadrian's Wall, and it seems to have fallen out of use about 180 AD.

It has been conjectured, and seems quite probable, that the Romans remained so long on the river Conwy because of their interest in British pearls. The pearl industry on the Conwy is undoubtedly ancient, and remained in being until modern times. Another even more likely reason for their continued presence is the richness of the copper and iron deposits nearby, notably the prehistoric copper workings on the Great Orme, which the Romans certainly knew of, and the seams of lead and iron above Trefriw may also have caught their attention.

Whatever the reason for their continued presence, it was the fact that they not only came but also stayed for some considerable time that put northern Wales, from an early period, on the world's map. It gave a period of peace and protection during which a settled pattern of land-use and order could emerge. We know that the collapse of this stability was so striking when the Romans left as to be thought of as a national crisis.

3 *The Headwaters of History*

Just as the Roman decision set a possible location for the
crossing inland, it was as a result of the collapse of the
Roman system in the period of post-Roman decline that
the focus shifted away from the area and towards the
coast. We might have inherited a pattern of settlement
centred on Caerhun, had it not been for the onslaught of
seaborne raiders flooding across the Irish Sea as soon as
the land was undefended.

The inability of the British to co-operate to defend
themselves had struck the Romans from the start, and
sure enough as soon as imposed central government was
withdrawn they reverted to their natural habit of fighting
each other. As a result there was little or no cohesion in
post-Roman Wales, or indeed in post-Roman Britain as a
whole. This situation would eventually lead to a flood of
immigrants from Jutland and Schleswig-Holstein, on the
east coast; on the west, it led at once to colonisation from
Ireland.

The raids started to become serious in the 360s and by
395 the whole of the land between the Conwy and the
Dee was overrun. About the turn of the fourth to fifth
centuries somebody arranged for a contingent of the
northern British tribe, the Gododdin, to come south to
northern Wales to turn the tide of invasion. Several things
about this are historically revealing. Firstly, the Gododdin
were evidently better able to deal with such situations
than the people of this area; it could be that they had not
been 'pacified' to the same extent and made weak by the
strength of Roman rule. Secondly the organisation of the

*The outcrop above the river mouth, now known as Vardre,
was an easily defended site in early times.*

move itself reveals that somebody was still able to oversee the British situation as a whole.

Who this was we do not, and cannot, know. The name of the leader of the warband, however, has come down to us. The contingent of the Gododdin which arrived in northern Wales is collectively known as Cunedda and his sons.

Tradition also tells us that Cunedda based his headquarters at Deganwy, on the high round hill known as the Vardre where so many later fortresses were to be sited for the same purpose. It is because it overlooks the approaches to the coast from the west, and because it was from this direction that the pressing and current threat arose, that this hill above the mouth of the Conwy river became the focus of the next few centuries of the area's history.

Cunedda's arrival at Deganwy is crucial to British history in more than one respect. If he and his descendants had not turned back the invaders, northern Wales would have become an Irish colony, like Scotland, instead of the native British territory which it still remains. His descendants at Deganwy became kings of Gwynedd, and the later independent Princes of Wales, Rhodri Mawr, Hywel Dda, Llywelyn Fawr and the last Llywelyn could trace their ancestry directly back to them, and so to him. Moreover the royal English house of York, through marriage of the Mortimer family into the house of Llywelyn the Great, and also through the line of Hywel Dda the royal house of Tudor, and hence the present English monarchy through several of its lines of descent, all trace their ancestry back to the kings of Gwynedd, and therefore to Cunedda and the tribe of the Gododdin.

Anyone standing on the Vardre even now, with its bird's-eye view of the river and the bay, can see that this is no slight place. Whether or not Cunedda was the first to build a castle there, in about the year 400, we know for certain that it had a history as a seat of power and a place of great events which spanned a period of at least seven hundred years. When Conwy castle was first built, Deganwy was already older than Conwy is today.

When the site of Deganwy castle on the Vardre was excavated in the first half of the 1960s by Leslie Alcock for the University of Wales, finds there ran back to the Roman period, in the form of pottery and coins, indicating the occupation of the site as perhaps a look-out post on the coast to complement the valley fort. As proof of the validity of the tradition that this was the seat of Maelgwn Gwynedd, descendant of Cunedda and ancestor of the royal lines, some datable shreds of imported Mediterranean pottery, originally wine jars, show that during the late fifth or early sixth century there was a prosperous and sophisticated court here.

Maelgwn is too real a figure to belong solely to folklore. Tall, irascible, licentious, the figure we can see looking out from Deganwy, over this river crossing by which he controlled the heartland of Gwynedd, is a fearsome one, and nothing if not human. The details come to us from the historian Gildas, who knew him personally. The body of folklore which has gathered round him is collected in later sources, in works such as the Red Book of Hergest, the manuscript of which is of late-14th or early-15th century date, though the material may of course be partly very much older. Maelgwn is said in the Welsh Annals to have died in 547 AD, and since these Easter tables may well go back in their original form to the year which they record we must give a certain amount of credence to this.

The stories of Maelgwn and his court on the Conwy river are a valuable part of our national tradition. One in particular concerns us here, since it appears to describe what must be the first recorded instance of a crossing of the river.

The story contains another first, since it says that it was Maelgwn who held the first eisteddfod, that essentially Welsh cultural feature, the musical and literary competition which still takes place locally and nationally to this day. In the instance in question, he had decided to hold the event across the river, on Conwy Mountain.

The king had a possible hidden motive in choosing the site. He himself favoured the bards, and wanted them to out-do the harpists. He therefore removed all the boats, forcing the competitors to swim from Deganwy, with the result that the bards arrived at the competition refreshed and in good voice, the musicians with the strings of their instruments ruined by the salt water.

Once in place, a castle attracts history. The very existence of the fortress at Deganwy ensured an eventful future for the place. It was, we are told, burnt down by lightning in 812, a hazard in the days when buildings were mainly made of wood. According to the Welsh Annals, the Saxons destroyed Deganwy again in 822, an event which was in fact a raid by Ceolwulf, the Anglian king of Mercia (who would have been horrified to have been referred to as a Saxon), who was continuing his country's attempt to annex northern Wales to Mercia. He succeeded to some extent with Powys, but once again the Conwy river proved a limiting point and the ultimate protection of the heartland of Gwynedd.

The Anglo-Saxon chronicle mentions a similar attack on northern Wales, this time by the West Saxons under Egbert, in the year 830. Though far away from the main events of history, we were not to be left alone. Visitors were again on the Conwy in 880, Mercians once more on this occasion, when (according to Camden) a fierce battle took place on the point known as Cymryd, a little upriver from Conwy. Anarawd, leader of the Welsh, defeated Edred of Mercia and drove the invaders home. The event was termed 'Dial Rhodri', Rhodri's revenge, since Anarawd's father, Rhodri the Great, had been killed by the Saxons in 877.

The date of the first stone-built castle at Deganwy is unclear, since no remains have been found of that built by Robert of Rhuddlan, in the 1070s, a Norman Marcher lord who was killed at Deganwy in 1099 attempting (in an extraordinary feat of courage) to defend his possessions single-handed against a raid by the Welsh. It is in 1188, when Gerald of Wales crossed the Conwy in the company of Archbishop Baldwin, on a progress through Wales to raise support for the Third Crusade, that we next hear the name Deganwy.

When Gerald crossed the river Conwy there was already a presence on the western bank: the Abbey of Aberconwy. The Cistercian monks had come there precisely because it was inaccessible; they always favoured peaceful, and therefore often beautiful, spots. It was their policy to be a self-sufficient community, and on the far bank of the Conwy they no doubt thought they could fish and farm and pray in peace.

The Abbey received its charter from Llywelyn the Great in 1189, but evidently it was constructed and in use a few years earlier, since Gerald found it in place. He is returning from Anglesey, bound for Rhuddlan, at the time:

Having crossed the river Conwy, or rather an arm of the sea under Deganwy, leaving the Cistercian monastery of Conwy on the western bank of the river to our right hand, we arrived at Ruthlan . . .

It is a somewhat disappointing reference to our subject from this early source. Gerald does mention, a few chapters later (after which he became diverted by the stories of Merlin) that the river Conwy 'preserves it water unadulterated by the sea', a version, presumably, of the enduring legend that fresh water can be found far out in the bay.

We are now into a period of history, post-1066, which is more familiar to most of us, the period of the expansion of the Norman rule over Britain. In southern Wales, occupation by the Norman barons took place fast and overall. In northern Wales, this occurred in the marches around Chester, that disputed border country which proved something of a battlefield for the next centuries. The river Conwy once again, and crucially, proved to be the limiting factor. Beyond it, the mountainous heartland remained largely uninvaded, and the Earls and later the Kings of England looked out from Deganwy at a foreign land.

Thus several invasions stopped at the Conwy. In 1211, King John brought his army to the defence of the Earl of Chester in his long-running dispute with Llywelyn, Prince of Wales.

The castle at Deganwy had been destroyed by Llywelyn the Great as being too useful to the English, but was rebuilt by the Earl at once. His incursion into Gwynedd in the process was the trigger which set off a new attack by Llywelyn. In spite of Llywelyn's efforts, it was at the new castle at Deganwy that the royal army encamped.

The king at once found himself besieged, since the Welsh had control of the sea approach and could moreover cut off his land supplies from Chester. Many of the English soldiers starved, the survivors being reduced to eating their horses, and it was in a poor and ignominious state that King John and a reduced army retreated to England.

The English however retained control of the castle, if not of the river crossing, since it was finally taken by Llywelyn in 1213. Deganwy castle was then destroyed by the Welsh for the second time in 1241, when the border troubles became active again, and sure enough for the second time it was rebuilt by the English.

It was King John's son, Henry III, who decided to subdue the Welsh, and once again in 1245 an English army arrived at Deganwy. The barrier of the river

Only small fragments of masonry now remain of the several castles built on this hilltop during the Middle Ages.

confronted them then for ten weeks, while they grew cold and hungry. The striking event is conveyed to us in some detail in a letter written by a soldier to a friend in England, in September 1245:

His Majesty the king, with his army, is encamped at Gannock for the purpose of fortifying a castle which is now built in a most striking position there: and we are dwelling round it in tents, employed in watching, fasting, and praying, and amidst cold and nakedness. In watching, through fear of the Welsh suddenly attacking us by night; in fasting, because of a deficiency of provisions, the half-penny loaf being now risen to five pence; in prayings, that we may soon return safe and scot free home; and we are oppressed by cold and nakedness, because our houses are of canvas, and we are without winter clothing. There is a small arm of the sea, which ebbs and flows under the aforesaid castle (where we are staying), and forming a sort of harbour, into which, during our stay here, ships have often come from Ireland, and from Chester, bringing provisions. This arm of the sea lies between us and Snowdon, where the Welsh quarter themselves, and is, at high tide, about a crossbow-shot wide.

The letter proceeds to describe one of the few events of the long and unpleasant vigil. A ship bringing provisions went aground by accident on the further bank of the Conwy, and was at once attacked by the Welsh. The Normans crossed the river, along with Welsh troops from the border, to defend it, and chased the attackers into the hills. Returning to the river they then behaved inexcusably:

. . . and, like greedy and needy men, indulged in plunder, and spread fire and rapine through the country on the other side of the water, and, amongst other profane-proceedings, they irreverently pillaged a convent of the Cistercians, called Aberconwy, of all its property, and even of the chalices and books, and burnt the buildings belonging to it.

For this vandalism and sacrilege they received an equally horrifying reward. The Welsh gathered their forces and overtook the returning Normans, who had crossed without their horses and were now also burdened with the spoils:

> some of our people, choosing rather to trust to the mercy of the waves, and to perish by drowning, than to be slain at will by their enemies, threw themselves of their own accord into the waves, there to perish.

Some however, fell prisoner to the Welsh, now justifiably incensed. They hanged, beheaded and dismembered them.

> ... finally, they tore their miserable corpses limb from limb, and threw them into the water, in detestation of their wicked greediness in not sparing the church, especially one belonging to religious men.

After this bloodstained excursion, which must have been bitterly regretted by both sides, circumstances deteriorated further for the English army, until:

> there was no wine in the king's house, and indeed, not amongst the whole army, except one cask only; a measure of corn cost twenty shillings, a pasture ox three or four marks, and a hen was sold for eightpence. Men and horses consequently pined away, and numbers perished from want.

The king returned to England, leaving many of the bodies of his troops unburied. The castle, however, remained an English fortress, and seven years later, in 1252, Henry issued a charter of Deganwy, still then known as 'Gannoc', making it a free borough, some thirty-two years earlier than Conwy received the same honour from his son.

Two years later, Henry gave much of the borderland to his eldest son, Prince Edward, the future Edward I, and the castle on the east bank of the Conwy, at that time known as Gannoe, was included. The prince came to visit it in 1256, in his new capacity of Earl of Chester (a title still borne by the heir to the throne). Then for the first time, the future conqueror of Wales looked out over the Conwy, and perhaps conceived his fateful strategy. His father visited the site again in 1258, and again was obliged to retreat. The castle was in a state of virtual siege from 1257 until it finally fell to the Welsh in 1263.

Llywelyn ap Gruffudd, last independent Prince of Wales, then took a familiar step. He mined the walls and completely demolished the castle, which had proved so tempting to the Normans based in Chester. When Edward I came on the first of his campaigns to subdue Wales, and camped at Deganwy in 1277, there was no fortification left. Much of Wales' history results from his decision then. Unlike his predecessors he would not rebuild Deganwy. Instead he would plant a fortress on the further bank, from where he could control the crossing of the Conwy and the harbour entry, and from where he could launch his power into the heartland of Gwynedd.

4 The Great Irish Road

Once in place, of course, Conwy became the focus of the river crossing. This had not always been the favoured place to cross. Indeed the troops of Edward I approached the spot down the west bank of river, cutting their way through the ancient woodland which ran down to the foreshore. Edward's decision to build at Conwy relied on his being able to control that bank, and it was not until Dolwyddelan castle, always a Welsh stronghold, fell to his attacks in January 1283, that he could begin to move into the western sector of northern Wales beyond the Conwy.

The Conwy was traditionally crossed by ferry at

Once the castle was built, the focus of the river crossing moved from Deganwy to the foot of new town at Conwy.

Deganwy, since that was the narrowest point and the site of the earlier fortress, and therefore presumably of most activity. We have seen that that was where Giraldus and the Archbishop crossed in 1188, and it is reasonable to suppose that the ferry was well established even by then. It is quite some time before we hear of any other crossing. Although the Romans probably instituted a ferry near Tal-y-cafn we have no records of it, the first definite evidence for one there being in 1301.

There are indications that a commercial ferry was operating on the Conwy somewhere in 1189, since in that year the Charter which Llywelyn the Great gave to the monks of the monastery of Aberconwy specifically gives them the right to free passage across the rivers in the territory he controlled, the Conwy river among them. In fact Llywelyn gives them the complete use of the river:

> Also I have granted to the same monks all the water of the Conwy, and transit of the same water, and the fishery from Abergyffin unto Aberconwy.

This they were to enjoy for less than a hundred years. We know that when Edward I moved the monastery from Conwy to Maenan in 1283, he renewed many of the rights and privileges given them by Llywelyn. He even renewed that right of cost-free passage of the river; but the ferries and the fisheries of the river mouth were now under the king's control, and the boat now crossed, as it was to do for centuries to come, to the foreshore of the fortress town itself.

It is interesting to find that in the early records of the

47

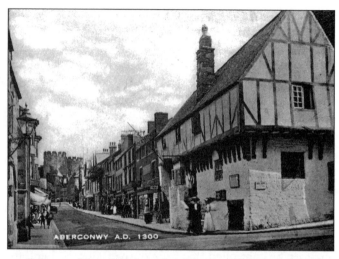

Only one of the original merchant's houses, Aberconwy House,
now remains from the period when Conwy became an
important posting and trading point.

ferry the township on the eastern side of the river is still
referred to as 'Gannow' or 'Cannok'. During the 15th
century it came to be known also as Vaerdref. The name
Vardre now refers only to the hill on which Deganwy
castle stood, but seems at one time to have been the name
of a wider area. It probably derives from Maer-dre,
'Mayor-town', presumably from its ancient status as a
borough. The name Deganwy was (as we have seen)
known to Giraldus, but seems to have been seldom used.
It remains something of a mystery, and the many
attempts to explain it are unsatisfactory. Clearly the 'gan'
part is related to Gannow and Canovium and therefore
presumably to Conwy, as the name of the river, but the

*Records of the ferry at Tal-y-cafn date from the Middle Ages
and this ferry continued in use until the 19th century.*

meaning would therefore seem to be 'south Ganno', and
this, if correct, would be puzzling, as it lies on the
northern bank of the estuary and at the river's northern
end.

Because of its close association with the castle during
the 14th century, the century after its transfer to Conwy,
the ferry is well recorded during this time. Two shillings
and eight pence were spent repairing the boat in 1301,
and in 1307 it needed twelve new oars, which set back the
current operator, one of the castle's bailiffs, the sum of
four shillings.

Details of the ferry at Tal-y-cafn become available also
from the 14th century, and we find that its boat had to be

The Llanrwst bridge, built in 1636, is one of the earliest bridges across the Conwy and remains the only traffic crossing at this point today.

renewed in 1326, since it was 'rotten from age' (but nevertheless apparently still worth 2s 6d). From the autumn of 1429 the two ferries, at Conwy and Tal-y-cafn, are operated as one business. They catered for the two alternatives for the route from England to Anglesey and Ireland from Chester, a route later referred to as 'the old Chester road'. You could follow the line of the Roman road and pitched down to Tal-y-cafn, then cross the hills by Bwlch-y-ddeufaen as the Romans did, in which case you would use the Tal-y-cafn ferry. Or you could come down slightly further north, to what is now Glan Conwy Corner, to make use of 'Sarn y Mynach', the causeway which the monks had built across the marshes of the Afon

Ganol valley, presumably to link the monastery at Rhos with the Abbey of Aberconwy. Sarn y Mynach was for centuries the main approach to the Conwy ferry. It was this latter route which became the Great Irish Road.

From early times an alternative way from England to Anglesey was apparent, but it did not emerge as a direct competitor to the 'old Chester road' until the 18th century. That is, from the border town of Shrewsbury, via Llangollen and down the Conwy valley to Llanrwst.

We do not know for certain when the river Conwy was first bridged. We know that there was a bridge at Llanrwst, and had been for some time, in January 1627, because a dispute arose as to who should repair it (since it linked the two counties of Caernarfon and Denbigh), which had to be decided by a jury at Ruthin.

> . . . concerning the public and common bridge situated on the King's highway over the river Conway in the parish of Llarnwst, in co. Denbigh, commonly called Llanrwst Bridge, which is and for many years has been in the greatest decay, so that neither the King's subjects nor horses, carts, and carriages are able to come and go without great danger to life, to the common nuisance of all neighbours and other subjects of the King crossing there, and of fellow countrymen in the said county . . .

The jury not unreasonably found that the inhabitants of each county should repair the half of the bridge abutting upon that county.

This was of course not the splendid stone-built

Pont y Gwyddel (meaning 'The Irishman's Bridge') reminds us of the traffic for Ireland which used the old coaching route, the Great Irish Road.

structure there today, but that one is venerable enough. The two counties got together again in 1636 to construct it, at the cost of £1,000. It would be pleasant to be able to confirm the legend which insists that this lovely, triple-arched hump-back was designed by the great architect, Inigo Jones, and to record thus the start of a tradition of the association of designers of distinction with the crossing of the Conwy; but unfortunately there is no evidence whatsoever for this.

That the Conwy was forded as well as bridged is not only probable but is proved for us by place names. Penrhyd, for instance, above Tal-y-cafn on the eastern bank, means 'head of the ford'. Rhyd-y-creua, just below

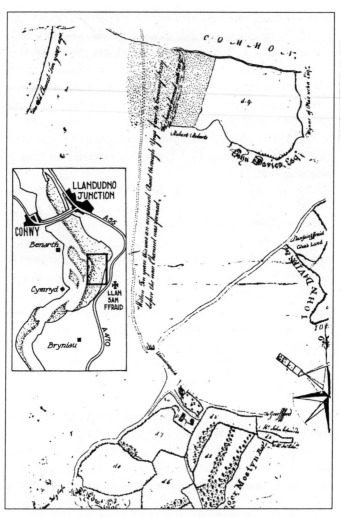

Old map showing track across the sands to Conwy ferry.

Betws-y-coed, means 'ford of the stepping stones'; the stones in question are still there. Less clear is the name Carreg-y-Groes, 'stones of the cross', on the river near Glan Conwy. It is sometimes said that this name indicates a fording point involving stepping stones, but the name 'groes' more commonly occurs in connection with crossroads, and one would expect to find 'carreg-y-rhyd' as the name of a river crossing. That there is no crossroad here perhaps means that the cross referred to was a religious one.

Already by the late 16th century there was a postal service, and the post to Ireland became a factor in the question of the road through northern Wales. By the end of that century, Holyhead was established as the port for the despatch of the royal mail. By the end of the next we know that the London to Holyhead road was an official route, with posting points all the way, since in 1675 it was surveyed for the king by John Ogilby, whose road maps form an invaluable insight into local and regional history. We see then the Great Irish Road pitching down from Denbigh to cross the marsh where Llandudno Junction now is by means of Sarn y Mynach to reach the Conwy ferry.

In its inland section, between Denbigh and the descent, the road shown by Ogilby is little used now, winding and tilting in the form of country lanes punctuated by old stone bridges at the intersecting streams. One of these midway between Llannefydd and Betws-yn-Rhos is significantly called Pont y Gwyddel ('Pontgwithey', in Ogilby), the Irishman's Bridge.

Beyond Conwy, in Ogilby's time, you had a choice,

which depended on whether the tide was in. If it was out you did not enter the town of Conwy at all, but passed through the gate in the curtain wall on the foreshore (the archway onto Lower Gate Street) and thence past the neck of Bodlondeb and across the Morfa, then out onto the broad stretch of sand which lies between Penmaenbach and Penmaenmawr. You stayed on the beach then much of the way to Anglesey, crossing Lavan Sands by a well-marked route to the ferry across the Menai to Beaumaris. It was a much shorter route than the alternative, or than the one in use today.

If you had to travel while the tide was in, Ogilby makes it clear that you passed through the walled town and took the Sychnant Pass, which was to remain the alternative route for centuries to come. You still had to negotiate Penmaenmawr, a precipitous and narrow way with terrifying exposure; and thence all the way round the coast to the Bangor ferry.

Coaches were a rare sight on the post roads at this time, and the arrival of one at the Conwy ferry must have caused quite a stir. Both the roads and the ferries were designed for travellers on horseback, which explains the frequent use of the sands, and consequently coach journeys were slow, uncomfortable, and full of dangers and breakdown.

Getting a coach by any means around Penmaenmawr seems to have been a particularly difficult task. On many tides the ebb was not sufficient to allow a passage around the beach. We have details of a journey made by Lord Clarendon, at the end of December in 1685. After two unsuccessful attempts to take his coach below

Penmaenmawr, in the face of a gale, they abandon it, and Lady Clarendon is carried over the mountain in a litter, the rest riding or walking. On the further side they were met by Lord Bulkeley's coach, which took them to Bangor and the ferry to Anglesey. In the meantime his own coach is due to be dismantled and carried over the mountain, although in the end by stringing the horses in single file while his men pushed, the coach and attendant wagon negotiate the mountain and join them in Anglesey.

By the middle of the next century all this has radically changed. It was, writes a certain William Morris in 1759: 'common these days to see two or three post chaises arriving at the same time' at Holyhead. He reports that as early as 1753 no less than eight wheeled vehicles left Chester in the space of forty-eight hours. An inexorable trend had started, the consequences of which we are living with today. The traffic problem was on the way.

It is from this period, the mid-18th century, that Conwy originates as a posting-point and travellers' lodging place, the main character which it has had for most of its later history. When travellers crossed on horseback they did not need to stop. They could time their journey to continue to Beaumaris, there was no need to change horses, and Conwy was ignored. When unwieldy coaches needed to be loaded and unloaded on the ferries, their horses rested, fed, or exchanged, their occupants similarly nourished and prepared for the onward journey and the hazards of Penmaenmawr, when the tide had to be right to pass the headland on the beach, and the weather fit, then a whole new trade came into being.

As early as 1748 two English gentlemen record that

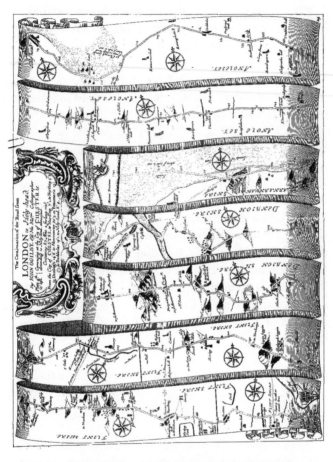

*The route of old coach road from Chester to Holyhead
as drawn by John Ogilby.*

travellers provide the main livelihood for the people of Conwy. The fare was good at their inn, however, although by the 1770s, when Wyndham came, the prices had become those of a tourist route

We are now in the great Irish road; the article of eating was doubled in our bills, and the door of our inn was crowded with beggars.

It was during the 18th century that the first adventurous tourists started to travel for the pleasure and interest of the journey rather than through business or in the course of political administration. As early as 1725 Daniel Defoe, the author of *Robinson Crusoe*, crossed the Conwy. He found the harbour noble, the river broad and deep. The best known traveller of all is perhaps Dr Johnson, who came this way with Mr and Mrs Thrale and their daughter, in the summer of 1774. We have some details of their visit to Conwy, and of its river and ferry, from his diary. It was 16th August, the day of the Conwy races:

It is now the day of the races at Conway, and the town is so full of company, that no money could procure lodgings.

They crossed the river in small boats, along with the passengers from the stage-coach, who were provided with lodgings, favoured no doubt þy advance booking. The delay overnight was caused by the fact that the tide allowed the passengers to cross in small boats, but not the coaches. Foot passengers, we know, were often ferried across at low tide.

> The tide did not serve the large ferry-boat, and therefore our coach could not very soon follow us.

The journey onwards filled the famous writer with trepidation – probably he had read Lord Clarendon's account – since the lack of accommodation might have meant crossing Penmaenmawr in the dark. However they seem to have delayed until dawn.

> Our coach was at last brought, and we set out with some anxiety, but we came to Penmaen Mawr by daylight; and found a way, lately made, very easy, and very safe.

The repair of the Penmaenmawr road is no doubt due to the institution of the stage-coach, certainly running by Dr Johnson's time and probably beginning in the 1760s. Stage-coaches had run from London to Chester for about a century, but the repair of the roads through mountainous northern Wales had to await an improved economy. The formation of turnpike trusts, by which local entrepreneurs built and maintained a stretch of road in return for tolls charged to its users, could only take place when there arose the likelihood of sufficient traffic to make it pay, and this chicken-and-egg situation was further exacerbated by difficult terrain.

Since Dr Johnson set out as soon as his coach was across, it seems that he must have travelled from Conwy

The Deganwy ferry shown above was popular with tourists until the early 20th century.

over the Sychnant Pass, since the high tide would have prevented the coach crossing the foreshore under Penmaenbach and a beach route at Penmaenmawr does not seem to have been considered. There is no doubt however that the stage-coach would have taken to the foreshore, being too large and heavy for the pass, with its precipitous fall to Dwygyfylchi, which would require it to leave Conwy later in the day. Hence also, no doubt, the importance of securing lodgings for its passengers.

The road over Penmaenmawr which Dr Johnson found, to his surprise, to be safe and well-made, was the result of much delay and debate. Pennant, in the 1770s records that:

In past times it was the terror of the traveller; extremely narrow, bad, and stoney; and what added to his fears, for a considerable way the danger increased with his progress, by reason of the precipice gaining additional height.

In 1769 Parliament was at last persuaded to grant £2,000 towards improving it, which enabled a turnpike trust to be set up for the stretch of road between the Conwy crossing and the Menai coast. The work took some three years, and hence had been finished for two years before Dr Johnson came. Pennant reports:

The road is now widened to a proper breadth, and near the verge of the precipice secured by a strong wall.

The road from the Tal-y-cafn ferry to Conwy, along the west bank, was improved at the same time.

When Pennant came to Conwy, a few years after Dr Johnson, he did not choose to cross there, but rather at Tal-y-cafn, since he was interested in seeing the Conwy valley and the ruins of Canovium. He does however throw some light on the place as it then was:

The town contains but few inhabitants, much of the ground within the walls being used for gardens.

The port then served the Conwy valley, doing a lively trade in the export of potatoes, in spite of the fact that, as he mentions, the approaches to the harbour were unsafe, 'on account of the sand-banks'.

It is from this period onwards that travellers begin to display a general dissatisfaction with the Conwy ferry. It was dangerous and delaying, and its use was made further unpleasant by the attitude and behaviour of the ferrymen. The bad impression which the people of Conwy caused by this means rankled for decades. William Bingley, towards the end of that century, sums the matter up:

> Most of the travellers who have crossed here (except the passengers in the Mail coach, who, by order of the post office, have a boat always waiting for them), know what it is to experience the wilful delays, and the gross and barefaced impositions of the ferry-men.

Adding injury to insult, they notoriously overcharged. Bingley continues:

> The charges ought to be a penny for every person on foot, except with respect to those who come in the public coaches or in post chaises, who are required, though from what principle I cannot learn, to pay a shilling each; two pence for a man and a horse, and half a crown a wheel for gentlemen's carriages. Instead of the latter fare, I have myself known them with the most impudent assurance possible, charge half a guinea for ferrying over a gig, and after receiving that, importune in addition for liquor.

Because of the sheer unpleasantness of this, it became the custom to avoid Conwy as far as possible, by crossing at Tal-y-cafn:

Such as travel from Chester to Holyhead, sometimes go by a place called Bwlch-y-ddau-fain, thereby avoiding Conwy and Penmaenmawr.

writes an unnamed traveller in about 1770. And

by going this road you will avoid the Conwy Ferry, which is very disagreeable to strangers, and sometimes dangerous.

Conwy in any case was hardly worth a visit, if we may judge by John Byng's impression, in 1784:

Conwy is a poor mean place and only subsists on the travell thro' the town.

Because of all this it was not surprisingly decided to by-pass Conwy altogether, and consequently in 1777 the Caernarvon Turnpike Trust was granted authority by Parliament to build a road from Aber over Bwlch-y-ddeufaen to the Tal-y-cafn ferry. From there the road was to go in both directions, to Llanrwst and hence to England via Llangollen by means of a new turnpike from Llanrwst established in the same year, and to Sarn y Mynach to join the old Chester road. Joining both the new and the old Irish roads in this way to a Bwlch-y-ddeufaen crossing of the hills would solve several problems at once.

John Byng, in 1784, writes what might well have been Conwy's requiem:

This bad boatage, over a stream one mile broad, is one

of the causes of a new London road being open'd thro Llanrwst, which in a short time will eclipse the old Chester road.

5 *The Age of Engineers*

Two great changes took place in Europe during the 18th century which affected the demands for travel within the British Isles. The Industrial Revolution led to the mass movement of goods and the need for urgent business communications. On a different level, and with subtle and varied consequences, the French Revolution and the subsequent war with France put a stop to the wealthy travellers' custom of taking the 'Grand Tour'.

They came to Wales and Ireland instead. They discovered the romance and wild beauty of our native scenery. These, the 'picturesque travellers', were our first tourists. They stayed at the coaching inns which had become a regular and reliable feature of the countryside thanks to the need to serve and facilitate the stage-coach and the mail. These we may see at regular intervals along our route, such as the Hawk and Buckle at Llannefydd and the Wheatsheaf at Betws-yn-Rhos, where the Holyhead road mapped by Ogilby approached its pitch down to Sarn y Mynach.

On the west bank of the Conwy the Groes Hotel served the roads between the Llanrwst and Tal-y-cafn crossings (which met at that point), and Conwy with its many inns. The inland route through Bwlch-y-ddeufaen, which was, as we have seen, in use at the end of the 18th century as a preferable way of avoiding Conwy, was served by the Bedol at Tal-y-bont and the Bull up the road at Llanbedr. More remarkably there seems to have been an inn at the edge of the high pass, above Pont Hafodty Gwyn. The Ordnance Survey still names a ruin there as the White Hart.

*The Hawk and Buckle at Llannefydd served the
stage coach on its route in the 18th century.*

The Wheatsheaf at Betws-yn-Rhos is another of the posting points.

The ruins of the White Hart can still be seen on a remote hillside at the start of the mountain pass.

By the end of the 18th century the many pressing reasons for dissatisfaction with the ferry at Conwy combined to favour the building of an improved inland route. Speed had become a priority. By 1780 you could travel from London to Holyhead in only three days. The tide at Conwy caused delays which had a commercial cost; the ferrymen were unpleasant and they overcharged; moreover the thing was positively dangerous. Pennant records that some years before he came, over eighty people had perished in an accident, with only one survivor – perhaps a factor in his decision to cross at Tal-y-cafn. Early in the 19th century William Bingley writes:

> It is however in contemplation to erect a bridge across the stream . . . when all the inconveniences will at once be rectified.

The turnpike road across Bwlch-y-ddeufaen, given the go-ahead in 1777, never got constructed. Travellers continued to use the route of the Roman road, as we have seen, which was no doubt repaired from time to time at local expense. The money allocated proved insufficient to build a complete new road. The unsatisfactory situation continued until, at the beginning of the 19th century, two factors of quite different sorts combined to make the construction of a bridge at Conwy a matter of national importance.

The long troubled relationship of England and Ireland exploded in rebellion in the 1790s which was put down by the English-controlled executive which, at the time, formed the key element in the nominally independent Irish parliament. England's vulnerability during its war with France with a potential enemy island off its coast prompted William Pitt, the Prime Minister, to take precautionary action. In 1800 he proposed the Act of Union, by which Ireland's and England's parliaments would merge, with Ireland having a hundred members in the House of Commons and thirty-two peers in the Lords.

The Act became law on 1st January, 1801. The result, as far as we are concerned, was that a constant stream of important, or at least self-important, people was set in motion between London and Dublin. With a voice in Parliament, these people inevitably had influence.

Accidents, as we have seen, were by no means unknown on the Conwy ferry. What made the fatality of 1806 so traumatic and poignant was perhaps the fact that it took place on Christmas Day.

. . . owing to a heavy swell in the river, the boat conveying the Irish Mail, with eight passengers, the coachman, guard and a youth, about fifteen years of age, in all fifteen in number, including the boatman, was upset, and only two persons saved.

So a 19th century guide records. A tomb in Llanrhos churchyard marks the grave of one of the victims, and mentions the event.

Even before these local and international matters made the question of the Conwy ferry a matter of urgent national importance, there had been growing talk of a bridge. The engineer John Rennie (like his contemporary, Thomas Telford, a Scot, and a civil engineer of great distinction in the late 18th and early 19th centuries) was the first to submit a plan, consisting of an earth embankment part of the way across supplemented by a series of arches set on a causeway for the remainder of the way, on top of all of which would be the road. The remarkable thing about Rennie's scheme was that it then rose from river level to pass right through the castle. The estimated cost was £164,180. It is frightening to think that if he had been able to reduce this cost Conwy would have been effectively destroyed.

The bridging of the Conwy must always have been a matter of doubtful viability. The enormous expense would have to be justified, and there were, after all, alternatives. Coming from Shrewsbury by Llangollen, one could cross the river over Llanrwst bridge. From the 1790s onwards a still more direct route ran through Snowdonia. Lord Penrhyn had connected his Bethesda quarries to the coast at Llandygái and then, by the Nant Ffrancon pass, to Capel Curig. It is said that his loss of an election in Conwy to a local man prejudiced him against the town to the extent that he vowed that he would destroy it, that grass would grow on its streets and market square. It seems however that his joining up of the route from Pentrefoelas to Llandygái was for his own commercial interests, and only coincidentally proved suitable to carry the mail coach.

Further reason for doubting the wisdom of building Conwy bridge must have been the unsettled decision of the official port for Ireland. Holyhead had established predominance, but from the 17th century onwards it had had a rival in the form of the sheltered harbour on the Llŷn Peninsula at Porth Dinllaen. In 1802, Parliament approved the formation of the Porth Dinllaen Harbour Company, and as Madocks set about reclaiming Traeth Mawr, at the bottom of the Ffestiniog valley, the major obstacle to a road approach to Porth Dinllaen was removed. Entrepreneurs were at this time building substantial inns along the probable route from Shrewsbury to this port for Ireland, and it was not until 1839 that the matter was formally and finally decided in favour of Holyhead, and even then the decision depended on a casting vote.

Once again we see how great effects depend on such fine points. If the matter had been decided earlier, and the other way, Telford (once more) would not have built his embankment and the railway would not have followed him along the northern coast, with the results we have mentioned earlier – such as the building of seaside resorts equivalent to Llandudno and Colwyn Bay further south.

Lord Penrhyn's route, which eventually became the A5, was turnpiked in 1802 and in use as the route from Holyhead to London by 1805. It was the rise of Liverpool and Manchester which kept the Chester road in use, in spite of all the opposition. However, the Irish mail from these cities was diverted to the Shrewsbury coach, which it met at Chirk , from 1808, so that the Chester road only carried local mail for northern Wales. It is little wonder, then, that the first Parliamentary Committee to consider the plans for a bridge, which sat in 1810, postponed a decision, asking for more consideration of the inland crossing.

The schemes put forward by the 19th century engineers made use of the island in the middle of the river.

It was to the next committee, sitting in 1811, that Thomas Telford reported. He reviewed the state of the roads from London to northern Wales, and recommended improved routes. At the same time he proposed a bridge at Conwy, and submitted a detailed design.

Telford's original plan was quite unlike that eventually adopted. It consisted of a cast-iron arch from the town to the island, a series of arches across the island itself, a channel spanned by a drawbridge, and then the embankment roughly as it eventually was. The committee approved, but no action was taken. The scheme, though cheaper than Rennie's, must still have seemed financially unsound. It was to have cost £44,178.

As late as 1813 the ferry was causing annoyance and the alternative inland route was still in use. Richard Fenton writes, of his tour of that year:

> . . . we waited in vain for two hours for the ferry boat, the wind being too high to admit of its crossing, which obliged us to go all round to Tal-y-cafn; and then, through a most tempestuous night over Bwlch-y-ddwyfaen to Aber.

The promotion of the future A5, and the neglect of the old Chester road, continued into the second decade of the 19th century. It was not until 1820, in fact, that the parliamentary Select Committee considering the Holyhead road recommended bridging the Conwy – hardly, as we have seen, a new idea. Their reason was the importance of the Chester mail coach, which carried mail from Liverpool and Manchester. Evidently by 1820 this included again the Irish mail, which for a time had been switched to the Shrewsbury coach; the Committee report speaks of

> . . . the great importance of the Commercial Correspondence between Ireland and the Northern Counties of England . . .

Telford had started to build the Menai suspension bridge in 1819. He put forward a revised scheme for Conwy, using the same technique rather than his original arched bridge, in 1822. The Committee's recommendation of this was strongly worded. It appeared to them 'a great National object' which they considered 'peculiarly entitled to the support of Parliament'.

Suspension bridges made of ropes were a common feature of the upland areas of China and neighbouring countries from early times, and indeed are still in use both there and in Latin America. In China a form of chain bridge, using metal links, was developed as early as the first centuries AD, and there is evidence from his notebooks that Thomas Telford knew of the existence of the Chinese bridges.

Suspension bridges had been built in Britain during the 18th century, and in fact the Menai was the third notable bridge of this form in this country (the others being over the rivers Tees and Tweed). One had also been built in America in 1760. The principle is simple, that of suspension of a rigid deck by vertical rods connected to large linked chains slung between the towers at either

After several earlier schemes had been found too expensive, Telford's final solution took the form of a suspension bridge linking the island to the castle rock.

end. Telford's Conwy bridge has kept its original chains, supporting still its span of 327 feet. The towers do not of course take the full weight of the suspended deck, since the chains are anchored into bedrock both at the castle end and on the former island, where Telford also located his tollhouse. The original platform was replaced by the present one, which is stabilised by steel girders, in 1896.

The great care which Telford and his workforce took to preserve the metalwork has been rewarded. The iron was plunged when hot into linseed oil. The result was that whereas the Victorian additions were found to be badly corroded, when the National Trust undertook an extensive restoration in 1990, Telford's original work was still in good condition. The Trust has now removed the

*Telford took care to relate his new bridge
archiectually to the medieval castle.*

damaged Victorian work, and previously, in 1966, the
footbridge which was added in the early years of this
century.

The battlemented stonework of the towers and
archways, and also the parapets adjoining them, of finely
faced ashlar limestone, form a respectful reference to its
larger neighbour, Edward's castle. Telford was by nature
an architect, and his works always show a sensitive
consciousness of their location.

It is clear that the purpose of the bridge was to carry
the mail for Ireland from Liverpool, Manchester, Chester
and the north. It was evidently considered important to
retain a separate route for this, perhaps because diverting
it to join the London coach from Shrewsbury caused

delays. It is ironic, and a symptom of the way, throughout this story, events seem independent of human will, that this purpose became obsolete almost as soon as the bridge was built. It opened to traffic in July 1826. In August of the same year a fleet of mail packets started operating directly between Liverpool and Dublin, and the Post Office's commercial mail for Ireland no longer went by road through Wales.

Telford's new scheme involved, like the previous ones, the joining of the eastern bank to the island in the river by causeway. This is perhaps the feature of it which has had the most radical effect on the area. From late in the 18th century until the embankment was built the major port serving the Conwy valley was Glan Conwy. The deep current of the river ran down the eastern bank at that time. This had evidently not always been so, and Glan Conwy's life as a port cannot have been long lived. A map made for a local landowner in 1776 shows a large island between Glan Conwy and Conwy and a road running to it across the sands, from near to where the Conwy Vale hotel now stands. It bears the words

> Within ten years this was an occasional Road through Ynys Fawr to Conwy Ferry before the new Channel was formed.

The channel in question it shows passing through the island, Ynys Fawr: 'The channel formed with'n 10 yrs'; and across on the western side of the river we see: 'The old Channel Ten years ago.'

Until about 1766, then, the river flowed down the

During the mid-19th century, Conwy's role as a port became of increasing importance.

Benarth bank, as it does now. It then flowed either side of the castle island, as we can see from charts and maps, but the main channel was on the castle side. The sandbanks, however, changed, as indeed they do now; and Davies Griffith, writing in 1802, reports that at different times during his life he had been able to reach the island dryshod from either shore. Since the change which took place between 1766 and 1776 fell into this period, he may have been referring to that strange anomaly. What can have diverted the river towards Glan Conwy it is hard to imagine. In any event Telford's embankment then diverted it back, and Glan Conwy could no longer serve the area's imports and exports. One of the effects of this was the rise of Conwy as a port. Minerals from the valley slopes, slates from quarries above Llanrwst and Trefriw, timber from the Gwydir forest and farm produce from the fertile Conwy valley, which had left by sea from Glan Conwy in the 18th century, left in large quantities from Conwy in the 19th. To cater for this increasing trade the present quay was built by the Corporation, costing £1,300 in 1833.

The building of the embankment started at the same time as the bridge, in April 1822. Material was wheeled by labourers from the eastern bank. It took three years to construct, during which period it became apparent that it was having a radical effect on the river. The increased current on the Conwy side apparently washed away a road, which perhaps ran along the foreshore. The current between the extending embankment and the island increased greatly, to the danger of the ferry crossing, which of course still continued. In May 1825, the embankment (in all 2,015 feet long) reached the island, and at once the ferry journey was both eased and shortened. It merely crossed to the island, and vehicles could then proceed along the new embankment.

For more than a year then work continued. The improvement of the roads through Conwy, including the construction of a new arch and an exit from the town by a new route, across what was previously Conwy racecourse, together with work around the headland of Penmaenbach, presumably helped to mop up the workforce suddenly released by the completion of the embankment. The resident engineer for the whole project was a Mr William Provis, who also supervised the work at Menai, a young man whose career Telford wished to encourage.

The bridge, now restored to its original form by the National Trust, is a masterpiece not only of innovatory engineering but of architectural skill. Angled to relate to the castle as if it formed a drawbridge approach, it may be seen in its true elegance now only in old prints and photographs, before the view of it was blocked by the present road bridge. If the river had to be bridged at all, we were fortunate that it should be done with such finesse. Nevertheless one cannot help regretting the loss of the castle's natural waterside character, when it loomed on its rock over an undisturbed river at its foot.

One of the incidental costs of building the bridge was compensating the owner of the ferry. It belonged at the time to a Mr Williams, of Craig-y-don, and a price was agreed with the government commissioners. Mr Williams received £6,315. The whole enterprise, according to published accounts, including bridge and embankment, had cost £51,239.14.5.

The bridge was opened to public use on 1 July, 1826, six months after its greater contemporary at Menai. There does not appear to have been much in the way of public ceremony. Considerably greater was the event which celebrated its centenary, postponed from 1926 to 1927 because of the depression, when the whole town took part in a pageant representing scenes of Conwy's past.

If we think we live in times of rapid and radical change, we may put this in perspective by considering the world of surprises which broke over our ancestors a century and a half ago. Improvement in road transport by engineers such as Telford suddenly opened up the country to commercial and leisure traffic. Whole new towns, such as Llandudno, came into existence. Hard behind the road came the railway, the first mechanical means of locomotion. Everything that has happened since is only a gradual development compared to that one quantum leap, from horsepower to steam propulsion.

Robert Stephenson, the railway engineer, was the son of the great George Stephenson, the pioneer of steam locomotion. He managed his father's works, where the famous early engines were made, and both father and son were responsible for building railways as well as engines. Robert then branched out into civil engineering, and in the process designed and supervised the construction of many bridges, including one across the St Lawrence at Montreal and two over the Nile.

The bridge at Conwy was again a lesser companion to that at Menai, and both bridges were an integral part of the railway line from Chester to Holyhead, the extension of the London line which followed inevitably on the decision to make Holyhead the official port for Ireland, taken in 1839.

The first stone of the railway bridge was laid in June 1846. The bridge was built by what was then an innovatory technique, being largely prefabricated. The two vast tubes, each weighing some 1,300 tons, were built at a site slightly up-river and floated into position, then raised. Although he tested a model to destruction, the tubular structure was still viewed with suspicion, and Stephenson did not rely on the large tubes sustaining their own weight unaided. The bulk of the towers of the bridge, which makes it somewhat inelegant, was due to his expectation that the tubes would have to be supported

*The coming of the railway had a radical effect on travel in the 1840's
with the result that Stephenson's railway crossing followed hard on
the line of Telford's road. Just like the new Conwy tunnel,
Stephenson's tubular railway bridge was prefabricated in sections
upriver and floated into position. Two tubes were built,
each weighing 1300 tons and measuring 412 feet in length,
standing 18 feet above high water.*

from the towers by chains, in the manner of the
neighbouring suspension bridge. Government regulations
also still demanded the use of chains, at the time the
bridge was designed. When however the tubes did
eventually begin to sag, with the advent of heavier stock
towards the end of the last century, the solution favoured
was that of supporting them from underneath, by the
huge round pillars at either end of the bridge which now
reduce its overall span.

The first tube was ready to float and lift into place by the spring of 1848, and the second followed that November. The operation was a slow and tense one, involving six pontoons in the floating stage linked by chains to capstans on the bank. The tubes floated from their construction site four hundred yards upstream in a period of twenty minutes, but the raising into position took considerably longer. The first tube rose on 8th April by eight foot, a further six on 10th, and into its highest position – slightly above its bed, which was then completed – on 11th. The railway then operated through the single tube from 1st May, 1848. It only became a double-track crossing when the construction of the second tube was completed, and that was floated into place on 12th October and raised on 2nd November, finally being fixed in place on 8th December. The second line then became operational from 2nd January, 1849. The railway bridge had taken two years and seven months to build, at a total cost of £145,190.18.0.

The two tubes are anchored into the stone towers at the Conwy end, but free at the other to move on cast-iron rollers, to cater for possible expansion with changes of temperature. They are not uniformly rectangular, but bulge in the middle by some three feet.

Like Telford's Stephenson's new route had to breach the town walls. To do so he constructed an elegant skewed arch, for practical reasons in the Tudor style, with flattened top rather than a Gothic point, which might have been more appropriate in the setting.

While all this was going on work also took place on further engineering feats in Conwy, the tunnel under part of the town and the deep Cadnant cutting. Considering the construction of the whole railway took only three years the manpower involved in these big projects must have been considerable.

Unlike the Telford occasion, which seems to have gone largely without ceremony, Stephenson's achievement was celebrated with a public dinner, held at the back of the Castle Hotel in a special pavilion. This took place between the floating of the two sections, on 17th May, 1848. Stephenson himself was the guest of honour and made the main speech, with his father George, known as the father of railways, nearby at the top table.

It is now upwards of six or about seven years since I entertained the idea of constructing bridges with wrought-iron plates, rivetted together . . .

On that historic occasion Stephenson noted what must have been in the minds of many, that the world had changed. It must be unusual indeed for such change to be so directly the work of two men, in this case him and his father, both present in Conwy on that day:

. . . not thirty years ago, but even twenty-five, when we were dragged along at eight or ten, or perhaps twelve miles an hour, and the locomotive was then in its infancy; we have not only increased the ease of travelling, which the hon. Chairman alluded to, the armchair journey to London, but we are now whirled along at a speed exceeding that of the fleetest horse.

6 Modern Times

Telford's suspension bridge at Conwy was built to expedite the mail to Ireland. Stephenson's tubular bridge was built to serve the port of Holyhead. Their effects on northern Wales were incidental, unintended and unpredictable.

One thing these lines of communication did was fix the settlement pattern for the future along the north coast. Their construction coincided with the fashion for travelling to seaside watering places, an extension of the habit of visiting spas for the sake of health and leisure. Llandudno came into existence in the 1850s and grew to the size of a major resort during the 1880s. Colwyn Bay

With the increase in travel which followed the coming of the railway, seaside resorts like Llnadudno came suudenly into existance.

belongs mainly to the 1890s. Both were the product of the routing of the railway along the northern coast, following the decision to cross the Conwy near its mouth. The existence of the two towns led to further urbanisation, and minor resorts grew up nearby at Deganwy and Rhos-on-sea, Penmaenmawr, Abergele, Rhyl and so on. A largely anglicised population occupied the coastal strip, by contrast to the uninterrupted Welshness of the coast's immediate hinterland.

The valley was not neglected, but it could never again compete with the densely populated coast. In 1897 a bridge superseded the ancient ferry at Tal-y-cafn. Further up river Llanrwst has retained to the present day its agricultural character and its 17th century bridge across the river.

By the end of the 19th century northern Wales was well served by lines of communication. No doubt at this time most people still came by train; the fifth edition of Baddeley and Ward's *Thorough Guides*, published in 1895, gives the fares. It cost a princely 65/6 to take a 'tourist ticket' (presumably a return) from London to Conwy, first class. Third class you could do it for 33/-.

By the time the eighth edition came out, in 1909, there were definite signs of change. Train fares had decreased slightly, but ahead of them in the book is a supplement entitled 'Cycling and Motoring', followed by another on 'Coaches and Conveyances'. Among these is featured a 'Motor Omnibus Service', which specialised in routes from railway stations to places not served by railway. A little later the same firm published a guide to Llandudno and northern Wales which included a 'special section for

In 1897, a bridge finally replaced the ancient ferry at Tal-y-cafn.

motorists'. It is said there that 'nearly every visitor to the neighbourhood travels by car or coach over the famous highways of Snowdonia'. The age of mass travel, and particularly of travel purely for itself, had clearly got under way.

The result of this trend was that by the 1930s Conwy was once again in trouble. Telford's suspension bridge had operated as a toll bridge from the start; one tollhouse, in Castle Square, has been removed, but the other still stands at the island end of the bridge and houses the National Trust's Telford display. The need to collect the toll meant that as traffic increased so did the length of the queue, and it became clear that the old suspension bridge would not suffice forever in times of clearly increasing mobility. Moreover the town itself was holding the traffic up, as

The sudden increase in the use of motor vehicles during the 1920's and 1930's had a dramatic effect on the roads and town streets of North Wales.

well as suffering from it, with its narrow streets already congested with cars. The late 1930s anticipated the 1960s as a time of much road widening and straightening, and much bypassing, throughout Britain.

Once again the timing proved critical, and this time Conwy was saved from major destruction by the Second World War.

In 1938 a scheme was produced by the Ministry of Transport which would have effectively destroyed Conwy as a harbourside town. Incorporating the Llandudno Junction flyover and the modern road bridge, it swept down to the quay on the line of the present access road, and passed along in front of the town wall on structure, to enter a tunnel running from near the curtain wall as far as Bodlondeb drive.

There was massive concern in Conwy at this scheme, the fishermen in particular fearing they would lose their livelihood with the loss of the quay. These, particularly the mussel fishermen, were then a more significant part of the town's economy than they are today. There were at the time some ninety-six licensed mussel fishers, who landed each year something like six times the crop of the 1980s – 946 tonnes, as against, for instance, 182 tonnes in 1987.

The Member of Parliament for the constituency at the time, then part of Caernarfon Boroughs, was none other than Lloyd George, and with much publicity and his usual high profile he paid a visit to Conwy to meet the objectors, in March 1938.

Lloyd George told them where his own concerns lay. He was chiefly interested in employment, and the effect of the roadway on the scenery was of secondary importance as far as he was concerned. As the mussel fishermen feared their jobs would be affected this won the great man's sympathy, but he pointed out that as far as the effect on the town was concerned the alternative, which was favoured by the County Council, was even worse. This alternative was a scheme to take a widened road through the centre of the town, sweeping away the Guildhall and all the buildings on both sides of Rosehill Street, the *Erskine Hotel* and much of Lancaster Square, to a new wide arch in the town wall alongside Telford's Bangor Arch.

In 1939 a Public Inquiry was held at the Palace Cinema, Conwy, which lasted two days. Finally it was the

Before the Second World War, the mussel fishery at Conwy was an important element of the economy of the town.

quay route which became the subject of the 1940 Order, which ironically remained in force until it was superseded by the new Orders of the late 1970s. The year 1940 was of course no time to start building new roads, and while petrol rationing remained in force after the war, and the country set about restoring itself to economic health, the matter seemed less urgent.

The scheme did, however, go ahead in slow phases. In 1958 half of the proposed road bridge was constructed; the original plan was for this to be dual carriageway, which is why the back of the bridge to this day remains unfaced. The second half, which never got built, would have involved the demolition of Telford's masterpiece, which in any case was threatened by the inability of Conwy Borough Council to meet the cost of maintaining it, now that it would lack its income from tolls. The outcry at the proposal to demolish it was sufficient to force a Poll of Electors, which took place in January 1965. Ironically the result was a majority in favour of demolition, but the exercise had brought the issue to the attention of wider interests, and the National Trust held an appeal which, together with the handing over of £38,000 by the Council from the funds saved from the bridge's tolls, enabled it to acquire and repair the old bridge in 1965-6.

Conwy's latest bridge was originally designed by H.W. FitzSimons, who was responsible for many fine bridges, but he died in 1956 before it was constructed, and supervision of the work was taken on by C.W. Glover and Partners with Sir Percy Thomas as consulting architect. Construction was undertaken by the firm of Sir William Arrol & Co. Ltd., who started work in February

The present road bridge was finally constructed
between the years 1955 and 1958.

Surfacing the present road bridge

1955. The bridge was finished in December 1958 and opened on 13th December by the Rt Hon. Henry Brooke, MP, who was Minister for Welsh Affairs as part of his portfolio as Minister of Housing and Local Government.

The 1958 bridge is a single-span steel arch of 310 feet, felt by some to introduce an inappropriate curved line into a setting of verticals and horizontals. It has several other unfortunate effects. It separates the castle from its water base much more radically than did Telford's sensitive treatment. It blocks off the view of Telford's delicate structure. And of course, until the opening of the tunnel, without its planned continuation along the quay it perpetuated the fundamental mistake of directing the main road traffic straight into the town's narrow streets.

Born long after its intended time, it was out of date as soon as it was open.

By the 1960s it had become obvious that things were moving at an accelerating pace, and the country's infrastructure had to be overhauled to keep up with commercial progress. Yet looking back from the eventual outcome to the beginnings of it then we feel we are viewing a simpler and humbler world. Geared to a slower pace of change and more modest statistics, the authorities who then had responsibility for the roads of northern Wales could clearly not have foreseen the state of affairs with which we live now, only thirty years later.

In 1964 the Ministry of Transport (since Wales was then still run from Whitehall) held a meeting with officials of the Caernarfonshire County Council's Planning and Highways department, to discuss 'highway and allied planning problems in North Wales'. It was partly as a result of this meeting that the County Surveyor brought out, in 1966, a scheme for bridging the river at Deganwy, as an alternative to the hated 1940 Order for a road along the quay.

This Deganwy bridge was incorporated into the massive study carried out in the year 1966 by a working party commissioned by the Welsh Office and the county and borough councils of northern Wales. The report on their surveys was published in December 1967 under the title 'Colwyn Bay, Conwy and Llandudno Area Traffic Study', a mouthful which was quickly shortened to 'Collcon'.

The Collcon Report is a remarkable document, covering many aspects of the area, including population, land use and employment. Most of all it was an analysis of the traffic, both by volume and type. To determine also the origin and destination of vehicles in the area a series of interview-surveys were carried out with both residents and visitors. Using a sample selection process, a total of 1,940 households were visited, to question residents about the number and type of trips they made. During the first two weeks of August 1966, vehicles were stopped and interviews carried out at five stations distributed around the Collcon area, in addition to the home visits, building up a mass of statistical facts about how many of whom went where. The Collcon data was much more than a traffic count, and it revealed some surprising and significant facts.

Until the production of these figures with the publication of the report it had seemed to many people reasonable to suggest reviving the old inland route, the pass across the mountains taken by the Romans and by travellers up to the 19th century, and more recently by two power-lines, by a gas main, and by the CEGB's new high-voltage pylon line carrying electricity from the nuclear power stations to the national grid. The Collcon data finally disqualified this route, not on the basis of previous arguments about the gradients and the height, but simply by showing that it would not serve the required purpose of relieving the coast road of traffic.

To be precise, the results of the traffic surveys showed that in terms of the Collcon area, only 7.8% of trips were through trips. That is, that 58.6% of vehicles in the area were making trips which had their origins *and* destinations somewhere between the boundaries of

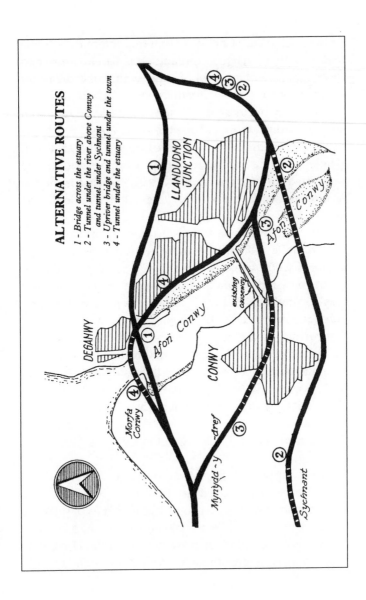

ALTERNATIVE ROUTES

1 - Bridge across the estuary
2 - Tunnel under the river above Conwy
    and tunnel under Sychnant
3 - Upriver bridge and tunnel under the town
4 - Tunnel under the estuary

DEGANWY

LLANDUDNO JUNCTION

Afon Conwy

Afon Conwy

Morfa Conwy

CONWY

Mynydd - y - dref

Sychnant

Colwyn Bay and Conwy – 'Internal-Internal' – while 33.6% either started outside this area and had destinations within it, or started within the area and finished outside it – 'Internal-External-Internal'. Only 7.8% of trips were of the 'External-External' type, both starting and finishing outside the study area.

Those are the percentages in terms of the area as a whole. Of the traffic crossing Conwy bridge the proportion of through traffic was 32.5%. That is, nearly 68% of cross-river traffic either originated or ended in the study area.

This was of course surprising to most of us. We had the impression that the traffic pouring over Conwy bridge (22,000 vehicles for an average August day in 1966) consisted *mainly* of visitors from England on their way to Anglesey and Llŷn. In fact it consisted then, and subsequently, mainly of people from Llandudno and Colwyn Bay going out for the day, and coming back. In the eastern part of the area traffic included also visitors from England coming to or from the resorts of Llandudno and Colwyn Bay. Those towns form the origin or destination, or both, of most of the area's traffic.

This finding underlined (as the Welsh Office Under-Secretary of State put it in a letter to Conwy's MP):

the simple fact . . . that traffic is generated by buildings. The great majority of road journeys are to and from places were people live (either as permanent residents or as holidaymakers), work, shop or seek entertainment. In North Wales west of the Dee by far the largest aggregations of population, holiday beds and places of entertainment are in the coastal strip from Prestatyn to Llanfairfechan.

All this meant that any new road which had as its purpose the relief of traffic congestion on the A55 and the freeing from traffic of the town centres of Colwyn Bay and Conwy must pass through the Collcon area. If it did not, it would relieve this coastal road of only 7.8% of its traffic, Conwy bridge and town of only 32$^1/_4$, and with the anticipated rate of growth (traffic volume being then expected to have more than doubled by 1986 to a figure of 50,000 vehicles per day on the proposed new road) the remaining local traffic would have risen, by 1986, to more than the total traffic for 1966. Had the inland road been built – expensive, damaging, and useless – things would then have been worse than they were before.

Because these were figures many people refused to understand them, and the inland route in fact was still promoted (as we shall see) by some objectors at the 1975 Public Inquire. For practical purposes it was however dead. Such is the effect of a change in the state of knowledge.

The Collcon Report considered two main possible routes, together with a link road to Llandudno. Both would run behind Llandudno Junction. The one south of Conwy would then have used the corridor originally protected in the 1940 Order for the road to Llandudno, crossed the river by the existing causeway and a new bridge south of the existing ones, to an elevated structure in the Gyffin valley. It would then pass through a tunnel under the top of the town wall, and (apparently being

97

designed to do the maximum damage to the amenities of Conwy) emerge in the Cadnant Park estate before entering a second tunnel near the Morfa.

This was of course an unnecessarily disruptive route, and the eventual 'Preferred Route' was a much-modified version of it. However the Collcon Report was nothing if not committed. It favoured the Deganwy crossing, the County Surveyor's route, and it brought the full weight of its statistics to bear in support of it.

The Collcon Deganwy route would have passed through Llanrhos near Woodlands School, now a housing estate, then swept down through Deganwy near the church to cross the road, on elevated structure, just down river of the station. It would have maintained its height in setting out across the river.

Something of the naivety of those times becomes apparent if we consider the figures, bearing in mind that eventually the northern Wales road cost some £200 million, and the Conwy crossing itself well over £100 million.

The cost of providing a 'Coastal' dual carriageway from Aber, passing south of Conwy Castle to connect to a new highway near Llandudno Junction, would be expected to be in the order of £10 million.

The construction of the Gyffin route, with its tunnels:

... would be very expensive, a notional estimate being in the order of £4 million.

The Deganwy route was, of course, the cheapest:

The estimated cost of this alternative amounts to some £3 million.

The evaluation of these alternatives had to be considered both in terms of their usefulness and of their damaging effects. It was clear that the Gyffin valley route need not be nearly as harmful to the environment as that planned by Collcon. A continuous tunnel emerging near the Park Hall Hotel would avoid the destruction of property. A bridge and road of modest proportions would have been largely out of sight in the Gyffin valley. The elevated structure cutting across the seaward view at Deganwy would have damaged Conwy's views as well as the environment of Deganwy. The arguments were more finely balanced than Collcon at first made it appear.

Moreover it could be argued that by providing a link with the Llanrwst road in the Gyffin valley that route could relieve Conwy of *all* its through traffic, whereas the Deganwy route would leave at least some – that from or to the western side of the Conwy valley – passing through the ancient town.

Those who favoured this route – which ultimately became the Secretary of State's Preferred Route – during the winter of 1970 to 1971 were still living mentally in the innocent, low-budget world of the 1960s. It was natural to imagine a low, inconspicuous bridge, behind the railway bridge and therefore out of sight from the main viewpoints of Conwy. Road junctions too could be visualised simply as no more than that, so that the idea of

The proposal for a crossing to the Gyffin valley included a bridge of a scale that would have dwarfed the castle.

the Llanrwst traffic getting on and off the new road in the Gyffin valley was not problematic.

Nobody could have envisaged the enormous scale of what was to be built. To fit a road of motorway proportions into the delicate and small-scale landscape of the Conwy estuary is, inevitably, to ruin something. When it was eventually apparent that the road would be vast, the debate focussed on what it was preferable to ruin. Local opinion in the Conwy area polarises easily. Opposing camps sprang up in defence of the setting of Conwy castle, on the one hand, and of the mouth of the river at Deganwy on the other.

In the meantime a further study, this time a practical feasibility study of the alternative routes, was undertaken. This was a continuation of the work of Collcon, examining in detail all the possible routes, forty-five in all, in three main corridors.

7 *Public Inquiry*

The consultants' report, in effect an updating of Collcon carried out by R. Travers Morgan & Partners, the eventual consultants for the project, was published in July 1972. It was both a Feasibility Study and the announcement of the Secretary of State's Preferred Route. What was not immediately apparent in the excitement of its publication, but became gradually more important as events developed, was that it contained two new pieces of information.

The first was the vast scale of the enterprise, which we have already referred to. No longer were we talking in single-figure millions as in the Collcon days. Of the four main routes considered the least costly was estimated at £31.7 million. The works themselves were such as to have inevitable impact on the area. The bridge over the Conwy proposed to link a new embankment across the river to the Gyffin valley would have dwarfed the castle. In one version of its design the tower from which it would be suspended reared above the castle's highest turret. In an alternative form of cantilevered arch, the sheer bulk of the road where it spanned the river made the castle visually insignificant.

The same would of course have applied to a bridge at Deganwy. This road was to be a full-scale motorway, and wherever it went it would dominate the landscape.

That was the first new point which the 1972 report brought home to us. There was, however a second piece of information revealed in its study of all possible options. Tucked away inconspicuously among the technical data were the words:

We have also investigated the possibility of crossing the estuary in tunnel. This is incorporated in Route 7 which by-passes Llandudno Junction on the south side and then proceeds along the east shore of the estuary to enter the tunnel near Deganwy pier. The tunnel emerges on Conwy Morfa.

No more is said about it, but the tunnel is included in the route evaluation, and we find out for the first time that it is feasible.

Previously it had been assumed that the notion of tunnelling under the Conwy was too ambitious to be seriously considered. In the meantime there had been developed in other parts of the world a new technique: the immersed tube tunnel. It was this that would in due course enable the tunnel to compete in the list of possible feasible routes. What was most conspicuous about it, in the meantime, in the table of comparative evaluation, was that it did the least damage to the environment.

The purpose of the Feasibility Study was to set out the Secretary of State's Preferred Route, as recommended to him by the consultants in the light of their research. There was, however, conflict between the two, as the report made clear. The consultants favoured a Deganwy bridge; the Secretary of State, then the Rt Hon. Peter Thomas MP (later Lord Thomas of Gwydir), preferred a crossing upriver of Conwy castle, the Gyffin valley route. As the report formed the basis for debate at the subsequent public inquiry, this division of views haunted the Welsh Office's case and may have assisted the eventual victory of those who favoured neither.

Rival groups had already emerged combating each of the two alternative bridges. In the middle were some, such as the local Civic Society, who opposed both bridges. When the Borough Council committed itself to promoting a tunnel option the task for the mediators became that of persuading the hostile groups to support the tunnel rather than attack the bridges.

The Public Inquiry into the proposed route lasted from 20th May, 1975 until 13th February, 1976, at one hundred and four days of sitting time, at the time the longest public inquiry ever held. Nobody who sat through those weeks and months of discussion could fail to be impressed at the thoroughness with which the whole subject was investigated.

Since everyone who had a point to make was ultimately heard, the matter became extremely complicated. Broadly, however, the Inquiry organised itself into four areas of subject. There were those who objected to the road as a whole on the grounds that it was undesirably large. There were objectors, led by Colwyn Borough Council, who opposed only the stretch through Colwyn Bay. Supporters of this objection included some who objected to the whole route, on the grounds that the inland route through Tal-y-cafn was preferable. There were then objectors to the Preferred Route at Conwy, who mostly put their cases in co-operation with Aberconwy Borough Council and in support of the Aberconwy tunnel route. There were some among these however who continued to favour a Deganwy bridge. Then there were objections to the route through Penmaenmawr and Llanfairfechan. Wherever any of these objectors put forward an alternative route it drew into the tangle a further strand, counter-objectors, who opposed the alternative and supported the Welsh Office route, or even put forward a counter-alternative. In such ways as these the issues spread and multiplied.

The case against the road as a whole (which confusingly was heard towards the end of the Inquiry) involved questioning the Welsh Office's methods of predicting traffic increase. Many assumptions were made – such as a steady rate of growth of the economy and no rise in real terms in the price of fuel – which, by 1975, were already beginning to look like fantasy. The traffic predictions were based on trends established before the fuel crisis of the early '70s. Before that the price of petrol had remained remarkably static, and traffic on the roads had increased steadily. The case against the road, as put by Transport 2000 and the Friends of the Earth, relied largely on faulting the prediction figures by questioning these assumptions.

It seemed, however, that it was government policy that traffic should increase. We know, with hindsight, that it has done, and in spite of the decline in the growth of the economy and the rise in cost of fuel, and it is not hard to see why. Demand for the use of cars is mainly controlled by the availability, and the cost, of alternatives; and it has been government policy to favour the building of roads to facilitate road travel, against the improving and subsidising of railways.

The predictions could thus be right, even though the assumptions on which they were based were wrong. They could be made to be right by means of controlling this factor of substitutability. The objectors to the scale of the road pointed out that no consideration occurred in the calculations of predicted traffic of what could be the case if government policy on this point changed, and altered the relation between the cost and ease of motoring and that of going by train. As was said in the case put by Transport 2000, as far as their computer model was concerned the Chester to Holyhead railway line did not exist. But government policy was regarded by the Inquiry as given, fixed, immutable. And government policy was to build roads and thus increase the use of cars.

In view of this, the objectors claimed, it was difficult to see what the predictions were for; their supposed role being to justify the size of the road, they themselves were the result of a policy of building such roads.

The objectors did not argue that no road at all should be built. The importance of by-passing the town centres of Colwyn Bay and Conwy was obvious. It was simply claimed that local by-passes could be built at considerably less financial cost, and less cost to the environment and the future character of northern Wales, and that if the traffic figures were wrong then these would suffice.

As the Welsh Office's decision letter makes clear, the case for the road was made watertight by disallowing any debate on government policy.

The Inspector concluded that the objection related basically to Government policy and that if Transport 2000 wished this policy to be changed it is a matter for them to persuade the Government to change it.

They have, of course, not succeeded in doing so, and we live with the results of that failure. We are, as we can see, becoming year by year more overrun by cars in direct proportion to the building of new roads.

The government of the time, and hence the Welsh Office, justified the enormous expense of building vast new roads by a technique known as Cost-Benefit-Analysis. This produces an economic outcome which shows that the road that they intend to build will actually render a hypothetical profit, when the right values have been put into the equation, and hence would be a sound investment for the people of Great Britain.

One of the main inputs in Cost-Benefit-Analysis is a value for time; it is largely the saving of time that enables the evaluation to show a profit. Destruction of the environment is not, as one might have thought reasonable, given a negative value, to be offset against the saving of time. It is in fact not considered at all. It is left out of the equation completely. By some twenty years later, steps were taken to rectify this plainly selective reasoning, by which time the road-building programme which it justified was largely complete. It is of course doubtful whether the cost to the environment can really ever reasonably be given a monetary value. It seemed, however, that if one were going to have an evaluation at all, the costs of pollution and destruction should somehow be included in it.

The objectors pointed to a number of possible disbenefits which might arise from the building of the road. It was claimed by the promoters that the road would benefit the tourist industry. Even they, however, agreed that it would lead mainly to an increase in day visitors, the one type of tourist least beneficial to the local economy. At the same time, the objectors claimed, it would open up the rural areas to the pressure of commuters and second home owners, putting up property prices beyond the reach of locals and thus increasing the change in population and the erosion of Welsh culture and identity. It now apears likely that these grim warnings are becoming reality.

The Inquiry actually started with objectors who were putting forward a totally inland route. This would have run from Ewloe, through Bodfari to arrive at the valley near Eglwysbach, a route in fact not unlike the pre-Telford coaching road. It would have crossed at Tal-y-cafn and passed through Bwlch-y-ddeufaen to descend to Aber. The totally inland route had, as we have seen, much historical respectability. As the Welsh Office pointed out, however, it would leave as much traffic on the present A55 as there was then, as well as having a devastating effect on the rural environment and costing an estimated £80 million more.

The Inquiry then proceeded at its ponderous pace to consider the Colwyn Bay alternatives. The complexities of this, involving objectors and counter-objectors – that is, supporters of the Welsh Office proposals – occupied the next few months. During the hot summer of 1975 it never occurred to those present that they would still be there the following year. Jokes were made during the summer about holding a Christmas party; when the Christmas party duly came, the Inspector cutting the cake, the Inquiry had acquired a life of its own. It seemed by then that it could well go on forever.

During the summer the Colwyn route and its alternatives had eventually been disposed of, and the Inquiry moved on to consider what many people felt was its main issue, the crossing of the Conwy.

The Inquiry started to deal with the part of the road from Llandudno Junction to Conwy Morfa at the end of June 1975. By October it had at last reached the further bank. Everyone was aware of the importance of the matters at stake, and the excitement of the debate reached peaks worthy of the river's history.

Part of the delay, surprising in view of the overwhelming support for the tunnel crossing, was due to the fact that there were several variants of it. The Welsh Office argued with decreasing conviction against them all. There was, firstly, its own version, which it had to maintain was the best way to cross, if a tunnel were chosen. The Borough Council's own tunnel route was designed to do the least damage. The Council for the Protection of Rural Wales put forward a further modification of the Aberconwy route. The Deganwy bridge made a brief reappearance as being the second preference of some of the bodies objecting, should the tunnel prove impossible. There was a tense hiatus in the general harmony while that issue was discussed, threatening as always to split the opposition.

In February 1976, the Inspector retired bearing a mountain of documents. Eventually he reported to the Secretary of State. Tension increased again when the Secretary of State of the time, John Morris, decided in December 1977 to approve of all the route except the section of the Conwy crossing. This he continued to consider further. What had actually happened was that he did not fully accept the Inspector's conclusions.

The Inspector recognised the 'massive opposition from national and local sources' to this part of the published route, but he thought its bad effects were limited to its incongruous appearance against the background of the castle and the effect of clutter caused by building yet another bridge. It would not, he thought, be incongruous against the background of the Gyffin valley, already spoilt by development.

The Inspector also concluded that the published route would be the most successful route in removing traffic from the streets of Conwy and Llandudno Junction; would be the most likely to meet the needs of the traveller; would be used to a greater extent than any alternative route, and would have the best economic assessment of all the routes considered.

He did not, however, go so far as to recommend adoption. He also declined to make any recommendations in relation to any of the alternatives. He noted that the difference in cost for a tunnel option would be an extra £10 million.

Many times at the Public Inquiry, the Inspector (himself a mathematician by training) had pressed witnesses to put a monetary figure on the value of the setting of Conwy castle. Rightly, the experts all refused. It is not, they argued, the sort of thing that you can express in pounds and pence. The question of whether saving the

*The long drawn-out Public Inquiry included its lighter moments –
the inspector and the assessor cut the cake at a Christmas party.*

setting of Conwy castle is worth £10 million is not a
question that makes sense.

The Inspector was accompanied throughout the
Inquiry by an Assessor, whose job it was to advise him on
planning and environmental matters. Strangely, and to
add to the complexity of the case, the Assessor came out
in favour of the Deganwy bridge, and in spite of the
Inspector's making no alternative recommendation he
did so forthrightly in his section of the report. The
Inspector himself wrote disparagingly of the Deganwy
bridge route: in his view the effects of this on Deganwy
would be worse than the published route's effects on
Gyffin.

Against the background of this uncertainty the

Secretary of State ordered a further study. He was, he said, attracted by the idea of a submersed tunnel. In December 1977 R. Travers Morgan and Partners, together with the specialists in immersed tube tunnels, Christiani and Nielsen, were commissioned to investigate the possible under-river routes. This led to a further period of breath-holding, and much rumour and speculation about the Welsh Office's intentions.

In May 1979 there was a change of government. It was thus that in due course the final decision fell to be made by the Rt Hon. Nicholas Edwards MP, later Lord Crickhowell. With what appeared to be a delay in the production of the latest report tension was rising. Early in the year 1980 rumours began to circulate that the cost and time-consumption of a tunnel crossing would lead the Welsh Office to decide on a bridge. In the spring of 1980 the British Road Federation (a powerful lobby group) was campaigning for urgent progress to be made on the northern Wales road, which in effect meant opting for a bridge rather than a tunnel. The new feasibility study, which came out in March, found a tunnel to be possible, but by now very much more expensive – £77 million, in November 1979 prices, £16 million more than the Preferred Route. Clearly the matter was still very much in the balance.

At the end of April 1980, letters from some fifteen prominent authorities nationwide urged the Secretary of State to avoid damaging

the setting of the most perfect surviving example of a medieval fortified town in Britain, and one which stands comparison with the best things of its kind on the continent of Europe.

In May, June and July these letters were followed by pleas from counterpart authorities worldwide. At the same time all local organisations demonstrated public opinion by passing a resolution in support of the tunnel and sending it to the Secretary of State. Nicholas Edwards came to northern Wales on his own, in secret, and walked around the area looking at the routes.

On 28th July, 1980 Mr Edwards made his announcement. He said:

A bridge would have an unacceptable impact on Conwy Castle and the town's walls, which have been preserved in so complete a form as to make them a monument of rare and exceptional value.

This courageous and enlightened decision finally taken by the Rt Hon. Nicholas Edwards was all the more surprising in that it ran counter to the views of many of his civil service advisers (who continued to favour a bridge crossing, and some of whom were still committed to the Deganwy bridge) and in some respects to the conclusions of the Public Inquiry Inspector.

On 5th September the Secretary of State announced that he had decided to withdraw the published orders for the Conwy crossing. Things then moved with a more decisive momentum. In May 1981, the Draft Scheme and Orders for the proposed tunnel route were published, and after a period for objection were adopted in 1982. The

Conwy Tunnel (Supplementary Powers) Act received the Royal Assent in March 1983, and after yet another delay while compulsory purchase orders were undertaken, tenders were invited in February 1986.

On 24th September, 1986 the contract for the Conwy crossing was awarded to a joint venture set up by the firms of Costain and Tarmac, at a sum of £102 million for the stretch of road including the river crossing and some five kilometres of approach road either side. The Conwy river had made history yet again. It was the largest single trunk road contract ever undertaken in Great Britain.

8 Euroroute 22

The tender price of £102 million was in 1986 figures, and the final cost was of course much greater. For one thing, the initial price did not include the purchase of land. Including that element brought the starting cost into the 150 millions. A rough current estimate would put the total cost as lying in the 170-180 millions, and the final cost may in the end have been higher than that. It was estimated by an informed authority that some £25 million of the original price had gone straight back into the local economy.

The upgrading of the A55 in general between Chester and Bangor in the meantime continued, though no doubt upstaged by the star player, the Conwy tunnel. It had in fact been going on for many years. The Abergele bypass was complete by 1968, and the bypassing of St Asaph followed. After that we saw, in that direction, Holywell and Northop bypassed, and then a realignment of the road up Rhuallt hill. In the westerly direction the same period saw the Bangor bypass and the completion of the dual carriageway beyond Aber all the way to the Britannia bridge across the Menai Strait. Penmaenmawr and Llanfairfechan were bypassed late in the 1980s, a new tunnel built at Penmaen-bach and subsequently one, as the Conwy tunnel opened, at Pen-y-clip.

All this was part of a plan set out in a Welsh Office paper, 'Wales: The Way Ahead', which was published in July 1967. The result was that by 1990 more than fifty miles of upgrading had taken place on the A55. In another Welsh Office paper, 'Roads in Wales, 1985', it was

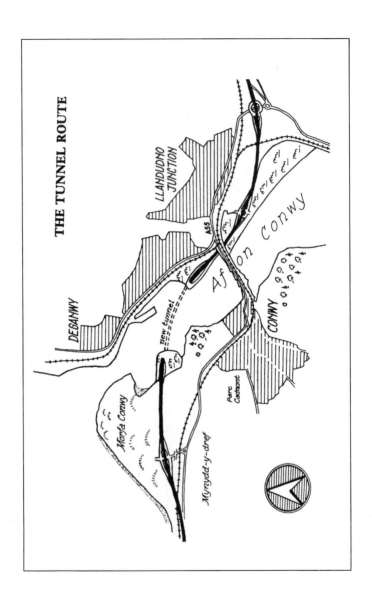

THE TUNNEL ROUTE

LLANDUDNO JUNCTION

DEGANWY

Afon Conwy

A55

New Tunnel

Morfa Conwy

Mynydd-y-dref

CONWY

Parc Cadnant

revealed that £300 million was to be spent on the trunk road between Glan Conwy and Aber alone.

In this immediate area, the most noticeable part of the scheme, before the Conwy tunnel, was the bypassing of Colwyn Bay. Started in September 1981, it was completed in two phases in 1984 and 1985. Involving constructing eleven bridges and diverting the railway, the project was only slightly less daunting than the building of the tunnel. A seawall of 22,000 precast interlocking units was built to protect the coastal road against storms, where it flanks the shore outside Llanddulas. These, known as 'dolos' units, have been much used in Holland. A twisted H in shape, they are strangely attractive objects, and one of them is formally on display in the forecourt of Colwyn Bay station. Apart from all this concrete, the road through Colwyn Bay used 1½ million tonnes of stone.

The new A55 was technically not a motorway. Its restrictions and standards are of a lower level. Consequently it has green signs rather than blue. Its importance lies in its status as part of one of the Euroroutes – a network ordained by the EC to link together, by road, its various capitals. Euroroute 22 joins London to (as far as possible) Dublin.

Work on the Glan Conwy to Conwy Morfa section had already started before the winter of 1986, the first phase being the reclamation of land between the causeway and Glan Conwy, to be used as a storage area for the large amount of spoil to come out of the trench for the tubes of the tunnel. The road was by then already constructed as far as Glan Conwy corner, from where (and through the reclaimed area) it could still have taken either the tunnel or the castle-bridge route. Next the basin was excavated where the tunnel sections were to be cast, an awesome hole in the river on the Morfa side protected by a high wall and dredged to a depth well below tide level: 10,000 square metres of excavation, forty-five feet deep and covering ten acres, about the size of Conwy itself. Work started first on the bunds protecting this and the eastern portal. The official commencement date was 3rd November, 1986.

Putting northern Wales on the world engineering map once again, this is Great Britain's first immersed tube tunnel. At 1,200 yards, or 1,090 metres, it consists of six reinforced concrete prefabricated units, each 118 metres long, 24 metres wide, 10.5 metres high, and each weighing 30,000 tonnes. These, together with cut-and-cover sections at each end, give the submerged crossing length of nearly three-quarters of a mile. By far the most spectacular part of the whole enterprise, at least for the layman, was the construction of these massive tubes in their casting basin, where they eventually sat like the hulls of ocean liners.

First a steel membrane was formed, which provided the final waterproof skin. The structural strength of the units lies in the concrete shell itself, which was cast within the membrane. Since the units were going to be sealed directly together, the plane of their ends had to be of extremely accurate alignment. The specification allowed for a tolerance of plus or minus three millimetres. In the end the average tolerance achieved was plus or minus two.

Work started on the first section in April 1988. The

sixth and last of them was completed in the summer of 1989, and at the end of August the basin was then slowly flooded. When the level inside the pool was at tide level, and the sections showed no more above the water than a few feet of their tops, the bund was breached. It had taken fifteen months in all to complete the casting.

In the meantime the sight of huge dredgers in the river had added to the sense of major activity, and Conwy became used to hearing Dutch spoken in its streets and pubs. By the time the casting basin was flooded the trench into which the sections were to go was excavated ready for them, together with a passage by which they were to reach it from the basin.

Work of course carried on as well with the approach roads. Lorries and dumpers carried material, seemingly, from place to place and back again. The figures involved are awe-inspiring, but ultimately beyond our normal comprehension. This phase of the road alone is said to have involved the use of 39,000 square meters of concrete. At peak, 1,200 people were directly employed on the site, and in addition some 150 supervising engineers, as well as the staff of about 100 working for the consultant engineers, R. Travers Morgan & Partners. These figures do not include the large labour force, a few hundred more, employed in bringing materials to the site.

The culmination point of the construction period was the floating out. Each of these sections, the size of liners, had to be precisely placed in its slot. In the end this demanding manoeuvre took place much as planned, but no doubt some fingernails were bitten at the time.

The floating relied on the calculated use of tides. On

The building of the road from Colwyn Bay to the Conwy river radically transformed the previous rural scene.

the high, spring tides flotation pontoons were floated onto the tops of the sections and secured, and there they sat when the tide ebbed. No tugs were used in the towing out of the sections. Instead there was an elaborate network of winches, hausers running between the pontoons on the sections and winches on the shore and on piled mooring points across the river, which was temporarily closed to traffic. The first section moved towards its resting-place on a dull, calm day, the 8th of December, 1989, after being moored for a week just outside the basin while it was prepared for immersion. It moved with unspectacular slowness, largely out of sight under the river's surface.

The movement into position took place on neap tides, winches on both sides hauling and restraining and, via the piled mooring points across the river, minutely controlling the section's movement into position. Once above the trench it stopped, while lines were adjusted according to instructions from survey points on the shore. The immersion took place at slack water. Observers above water could see almost nothing of the bulk of the section underneath the pontoons, the command tower fitted to the element when it was first moved out of the basin being the most conspicuous object showing above the water.

Out of sight under the surface the sinking took place over a period of days. The end which was to be joined, first to the fixed portal and later to the previous section, was lowered first, by means of filling the ballast banks inside it. When it was one metre down the 'tail' end was lowered to join it, and this process continued, metre by

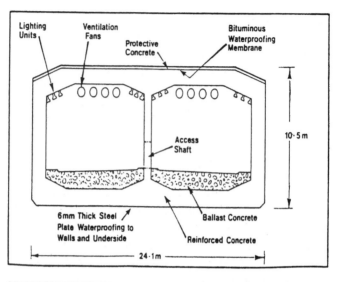

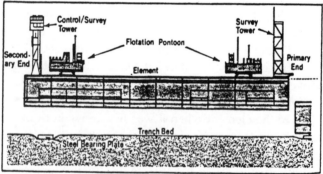

*An immersed tube tunnel consists of prefabricated sections
which are then floated into position and sealed together.*

The sections were constructed in an excavated casting basin on the west bank of the estuary.

The sections completed.

metre at a time, while its exact position was checked yet again.

Once in place the sections were sealed together by the compression of gaskets as two sections were pressed together by hydraulic rams fitted across their joining point. Finally an eight-hundred millimetre gap between the bottoms of the sections and the trench floor was filled with coarse sand-and cement clinker fill to act as a bed, pumped in with some difficulty in competition with accumulating silt. This, it is hoped, is designed to survive earth tremors during the tunnel's design life of 120 years.

The sections were then, as each was in place and sealed, completely buried in their trench, the riverbed being reinstated as far as possible at the same level as it was before. By May 1990 the link-up was complete.

*Figures in the foreground show the great size of the
sections being constructed in the casting basin.*

The original contract had been for a period of 221
weeks, or four and a quarter years. In spite of constant
rumours of delays the tunnel was substantially complete
within three and a half years of its commencement,
although it was still to be another year and a half before

*Once the sections were complete, the basin was flooded
and its wall eventually breached.*

the finishing touches enabled it to open to traffic. On 21st May, 1990, Mr Wyn Roberts, MP (subsequently the Rt Hon. Sir Wyn and later Lord Roberts of Conwy), Minister of State for Wales and Member of Parliament for Conwy, walked through the tunnel. Standing at the western portal on his emergence he paid tribute to the engineers and workforce who had achieved this remarkable and historic engineering feat.

In my capacity as Minister of State, I have attended ceremonies and functions of great national importance but I think this one ranks as one of the most memorable and one that I shall treasure in the years to come. It is, of course, the more special because of the close personal links I have as your constituency Member of Parliament.

We properly lay great store by earlier civil engineering feats of which we have three notable examples here in Conwy. In the foreground, we have Conwy Castle, built by Edward I in the mid-thirteenth century, which is a magnificent example of medieval architecture. We have Telford's lovely suspension bridge completed in 1826 and the only crossing for vehicles and pedestrians for 133 years. Finally, the twin steel tube railway bridge completed by Robert Stephenson in 1849.

What is being achieved with the Conwy Crossing is the parallel in modern engineering terms and will undoubtedly stand as a fitting monument to this time and age.

Acknowledgements

The Author wishes to thank Mr and Mrs Mitchell Pattinson for access to their archive material, and Mr John Harrison of R. Travers Morgan & Partners for his help in supplying information. An invaluable source book, for which he is indebted for some of the information contained in Chapter IV and V, is H.R. Davies' *The Conwy and the Menai Ferries*, published by the University of Wales Press.

Illustrations

The publishers wish to acknowledge the following for kindly allowing the reproduction of various photographs and prints:

Betty Pattinson, Conwy: cover, title page.
Cambridge University collection of air photographs:
pages 17, 25, 31, 35(a)
The Author: pages 24(a), 24(b), 52, 66(a) and (b), 67, 84,
91(a) and (b), 92, 100, 111, 120(a) and (b), 122,
123(a) and (b) 124, 125, 126(a) and (b)
E. Emrys Jones: pages 35(b), 50, 86
National Monuments Record of Wales: page 42
Gwasg Carreg Gwalch:
pages 16, 26, 46, 48, 60, 71, 74, 75, 77, 81, 89(a) and (b)
Gwynedd Archives Service: page 49
From a collection by the late E. O. Foulkes, Borough
Engineer and Surveyor and Engineer to the Conwy
Bridge Commissioners 1933-52: page 87